ROCKET

AIR CHIEF MARSHAL
SIR PHILIP JOUBERT DE LA FERTE

NEW YORK
PHILOSOPHICAL LIBRARY

Published, 1957, by
Philosophical Library, Inc.
15 East 40th Street, New York 16, N.Y.

PRINTED IN THE UNITED STATES OF AMERICA

CONTENTS

ILLUSTRATIONS

ACKNOWLEDGEMENTS

The contents of this book fall into two categories. The first part is historical and sets out to trace the development of rockets and rocket propulsion to the point where the threat to Britain's security from Hitler's V1 and V2 weapons was brought to nothing by the counter-measures of the Allies.

In writing this portion I have received assistance from the Air Ministry to the extent that I have been allowed to study the operations of a number of R.A.F. squadrons, and have been given access to the war diary of Flak Regiment 155W. From the Imperial War Museum have come the majority of the photographs. I am indebted to the Polish authorities in London for permission to publish extracts from the history of the Polish Air Force 1939–45. The names of others who have helped me are included in the text and to them I am most grateful.

The second part of the book is written in an attempt to analyse the effects, political and military, that long-range rockets carrying atomic or nuclear warheads can have on the policies of those nations that can produce and use them. The views expressed therein are entirely my own.

9

INTRODUCTION

This book has been written with two objects in view. The first is the payment of a just tribute to those officers and men of the Allied Air Forces who fought so bravely and with heavy loss to defeat the weapons V1 and V2, with which Hitler intended to destroy Britain and so win the war. The second is to draw attention to the many factors which affect the development of the defences of the free world in the years to come.

A number of arguments put forward are technical, but many more are political. No apology is made on this account for the following reasons.

In the past, weapons and armaments have developed without reference to politics or international thought. Boiling oil, molten lead, gunpowder, machine-guns, gas, tanks, and aircraft, were all brought into use without, at first, any consideration of the ethical aspect of their employment. The sole question asked was whether they would kill or maim so many of the enemy that victory would be achieved.

The creation of the megaton bomb, be it atomic or thermo-nuclear, has completely changed this situation. Today world opinion has a great deal to say on the subject of its employment. There are a vast number of political questions that enter into a consideration of its value, and the appropriateness of its use. It is therefore quite arguable that in any survey of the form that the national defence should take in the years to come must be based very largely on a broad political review of the world as it exists.

This is the reason for the shape that the later chapters of this book have taken, and for the apparent irrelevance of their content.

CHAPTER I

PEENEMÜNDE

The Birth of the Rocket

THE birth of the rocket, like that of Jeames de la Pluche, is "wrop in myst'ry". But with a little imagination it is possible to create a picture of a wrinkled Chinese firework-maker sitting cross-legged before his work-bench a thousand winters ago. He is filling a paper container with a gunpowder mixture. One end of the container he has closed and as he is about to close the other a wandering spark from his fire sets the container alight. To his astonishment and intense curiosity it shoots across the bench, leaving a trail of fire and smoke behind it. The next step of tying a container on to a stick and firing it into the air must have been quite short and thus he made the first rocket! So much for fantasy, but in any case it is an historical fact that the Chinese invented gunpowder, and from gunpowder to rockets the road is short. Charles Gibb-Smith in his fascinating book *A History of Flying* gives the date of the first use of rockets in war as 1232, when these weapons were fired by the Chinese at Mongols besieging the city of Kai-fung-fu. Three hundred years would not be too long a period of development, and so our picture of the early firework-maker and the date of his surprising discovery is reasonably accurate. News of the rocket and its application to warlike purposes was not long in reaching Europe. Roger Bacon gave a formula for the making of gunpowder some time in the early part of the 13th century, and a hundred and thirty years later rockets were used by the Paduans in battle at Chiozza (1379) and by the Venetians in 1380. Before then countless of these missiles must have been fired on days of rejoicing, and only soldiers may have thought of them as weapons. To the people at large they remained as a gay spectacle when kings were crowned or victories celebrated.

It was the Chinese again who conceived of a further use

for the rocket—as a vehicle. It is recounted that at some time
in the early 16th century a Chinese civil servant named Wan-
hoo designed the first jet aircraft. It was a combination of
kites connected by a saddle. Secured to the main structure
were a large number of rockets. Wan-hoo sat himself on the
saddle and gave the order to his workmen to light the touch-
paper. The rockets flamed, and in a cloud of fiery smoke
Wan-hoo departed rapidly and painfully to his ancestors. The
failure of this gallant experiment led to a certain amount of
discouragement amongst the "rocketeers".

But the germ was there and, according to certain authorities, in the Middle Ages rockets became a popular form of
weapon. In the 15th-century wars between France and England
they were used by the French, with apparently some lack of
success. In 1688 the Germans, with their love of the big
and the bigger, experimented with war rockets weighing a
hundredweight. There is also a suggestion, though perhaps
not a very substantial one, that the successful use of rockets
by Tippoo Sahib against British troops fighting in India
contributed to a local defeat. It is true, however, that the
Indians, like the Chinese, have always been very good at fire-
works, so perhaps the story is true. If so, then the development
of the British war rocket may have stemmed from this event.
In 1802 the then Colonel William Congreve began to study
the use of rockets as a weapon. He approached the War
Department but it was not interested. He then went to the
Board of Admiralty who were more forthcoming, providing
him with funds for his experiments. This money soon ran out,
so Congreve went back to the Army and this time was more
successful. By 1805 he was able to demonstrate to the authorities that his work had some value. As a result he was allowed,
in 1806, to bombard Boulogne with rockets fired from boats.
The fires which were started in the town burned for a day
and a night.

Congreve then persuaded the Army to form the first
Rocket Troop composed of 5 officers, 170 men and 160
horses, with a number of wheeled vehicles transporting the
rockets and their launching frames. He also had ideas for
using cavalry as rocket-launchers, and his views on attack and

defence by rocket ranged far and wide. He wrote two books on the subject which were published in 1814 and the basis of his theory of rocketry emerges as "the facility of firing a great number of rounds in a short time. . . ." He is at pains to say little about their lack of accuracy. Later a second Rocket Troop was formed.

Following on the Boulogne success Congreve rocket batteries were present in 1807 at Copenhagen; in 1809 in the Basque Roads, and against the American rebels at the Battle of Blankenberg in 1812. As a result the American Army established no less than ten rocket batteries in subsequent years.

At the Battle of Leipzig in 1813 the commander of the 2nd Rocket Troop, Captain Bogue, pushed his unit in advance of the main body of the Allies and bombarded a village held by five battalions of French infantry. The result was surprising—the garrison, terrified by this new weapon, evacuated the blazing village and between two and three thousand of them incontinently surrendered. Unfortunately, Bogue was killed at the moment of triumph. In 1812 Wellington had been offered the 2nd Rocket Troop for his Peninsula campaign, but had refused it. Now it was forced upon him and on at least one occasion it did good work in facilitating a river crossing in Southern France. But Wellington remained unconvinced, and soon after Waterloo the Troop was rearmed with 6-pounder guns. To this day, however, O Battery R.H.A. is known as the Rocket Troop since by an Army Order No. 112 of May 1901 it was authorized to assume and carry on the traditions of the original 2nd Rocket Troop which was "reduced" (modern disembodied) in 1816. At present O Battery is equipped with the 25-pounder Q.F. gun.

Though interest was maintained in rockets, mainly by Sir W. Congreve's writings, in the following years improvement in ballistics arising from the invention of the rifled gun[1] and the greater rate of fire achieved by breech-loading caused the rocket once more to fall into disrepute. But it did not die

[1] Wellington is reported to have said on seeing Congreve's rockets fired "if they had been invented before guns, what an improvement the latter would have been considered".

—in the 1914/18 war Le Prieur, a French inventor, produced a new form of the weapon that could be fired from aircraft, and before this the rocket had been used regularly in coast-guard services to carry rescue lines to stranded ships that could not be reached by other means.

In other fields we find a rocket car being made in 1928. The origin of this car has been attributed to the German motor firm of Opel. Contemporary photographs of a vehicle mounting a battery of rockets at the stern is clearly labelled "Volk-hart" and there are at least two references to a man named Max Valier as the driver and possibly also the designer. He apparently worked for the Opel firm on this project. By 1930 Valier had moved on from solid propellents to liquid fuel, and at that time he was obtaining remarkable acceleration and high speeds by burning a mixture of petrol and oxygen gas. He must have been a very brave man to dare to use this mixture at that date. The British Interplanetary Society had been watching Valier's experiments and in 1934 proposed that a rocket car using liquid fuel should be designed in England. This was to be the test-bed for more ambitious vehicles that some time later might convey space travellers to the moon. Before much progress was made the Hitler war intervened and the project was placed in cold storage.

In 1936 a Frenchman named Robert Esnault Pelterie who had carried out a certain amount of research on rockets made his data available to the British Government. He came from a family that had designed the R.E.P. monoplane which flew successfully in 1912. In 1929 the Opel rocket aircraft made a short flight and this machine may be regarded as the fore-runner of today's jet aeroplane.

In the late 1920s the German Army Weapons Depart-ment initiated research into the possibilities of producing a really long-range gun. By the Treaty of Versailles, a singularly unimaginative document, Germany's conventional armaments were severely restricted. Her land forces were not to exceed a certain very modest number, her navy was to be purely defensive in character, and her air force was banned altogether. In addition, her armament factories were under the closest supervision. Small wonder then that the clandestine

RIGHT: *Major-General Walter Dornberger surrenders to the United States Army*

BELOW: *Wernher von Braun, one of the senior scientists at Peenemünde*

V2 being prepared for launching

Crown Copyright

V1 in flight

Lieut.-Colonel Max Wachtel, Commander of Flak-Regiment W 155

German General Staff was looking for alternatives with which
to cheat the Treaty. The rocket offered such an alternative.
At first progress was slow. There was little data available on
which to base experiments. Fortunately for Germany there
was in the Weapons Department a certain Lieut.-Colonel
Dornberger. Dornberger had joined the Army in 1914, and
after a not particularly distinguished career as a regular officer,
found his way into the organization as a gunnery and ballistic
expert. He has written a book entitled *V2* which was published
after the Hitler war and which gives the impression that he
was the military head of the branch that developed the rocket
weapon. Other authorities state that Major-General Wolfgang
von Chamier-Glisczinski was the real head until he was killed
in the bomb raid on Peenemünde. He is referred to as of
Huguenot stock (there are Chamiers in England today) and
as being competent, though elderly and lacking in ambition.
In *The Second World War* Sir Winston Churchill quotes a
telegram from President Wilson which also refers to Chamier-
Glisczinski as the C.O. The name is garbled (the original
information came from Turkey) but it is clearly recognizable.[1]
The pattern of a competent though slow-moving senior officer
being pushed aside by an ambitious junior, a junior determined to have his own way in the development of the new
weapon—emerges quite clearly. First at Kummersdorf experimental station, in the early 1930s, and later, when the rocket
organization moved to Peenemünde, Dornberger claims,
probably with some justice, that he was the driving force
behind the whole project.

He was not the only man with vision, however, because a
combination of German scientists and industrialists was
working on another project, which had the same object in
view, the defeat of the terms of the Versailles Treaty. Lusser,
an engineer in the aeronautical firm of Fieseler at Cassel, was
designing the body of a flying bomb and "Ascania" was
working on its tail unit and controls. Later the firm of Argus
worked on a motor to drive the V1. So at least 15 years before

[1] In the telegram the name is given as Shemier-Gembeinski.
N.B.—One authority holds that General Professor Dr. Carl Becker
of the German Artillery was directly responsible for V2.

B

the Hitler war the design of the flying bomb was started, and it was in this weapon that the G.A.F. became interested. The Army was V2-minded! Dornberger, soon after he joined the Army Weapons Department, describes the situation which he found as "a muddle difficult to straighten out". Being a new entrant to the Ballistic Council of the Department it was natural that he should find everything wrong. Nevertheless, he seems to have had the right ideas. As he further describes the situation: "Neither industry nor any technical college was paying any attention to the development of high-powered rocket propulsion. There were only individual inventors who played about without financial support. . . ." Here it is possible to guess that Dornberger had a one-track mind. Much had already been achieved that was subsequently applied to the development of the V1—the flying bomb. These researches did not interest Dornberger, whose sole philosophy lay in the consideration of the long-range rocket. It is not quite clear from his book why he banked on liquid propulsion rather than on the use of solid fuel, but presumably he had already studied the subject very fully before he joined the Weapons Department. He may have dreamed at first of space travel and his association with Professor Oberth—the author of a book, *The Rocket into Interplanetary Space*, published in 1923—would support this idea. So as early as 1920/30[1] there was a powerful body in existence in Germany devoting its activities to the production of long-range weapons—the successors of Big Bertha, the gun with a range of 70 miles that bombarded Paris in 1918—and a possible alternative to the bombing aircraft on which so many people, Germans as well as other nationalities, were pinning their hopes.

In Britain the theory of strategical bombardment with long-range aircraft, a theory born in the 1914/18 war, held the field. So far as can be discovered there was no one in the service ministries even vaguely interested in a long-range rocket to be used as an offensive weapon. A small amount of research was devoted from 1935 onwards to producing an

[1] It must be appreciated that in many other countries research into rocket propulsion was proceeding at this time. A. R. Weyl's book *Guided Missiles* gives guidance as to the extent of these activities.

alternative to the expensive A.A. gun, and from this activity emerged the rocket batteries which for a while supplemented our meagre gun armament. This rocket was a short-range weapon using solid propellants and in no sense a substitute for the aeroplane.

It is clear that at this time in Britain, as opposed to Germany, neither thought nor research was being devoted to the development of long-range rocket projectiles. The Air Ministry was satisfied that its heavy bomber programme would meet all the foreseeable requirements of modern war.

So while the "shadow" aircraft factories were being built, and plans laid for the creation of the four-engined bomber force, Germany went ahead, first at Kummersdorf and later, as the new station became fully operative in 1937, at Peenemünde on the Baltic coast, with the great projects which produced the V1 and V2. These weapons, if they had come into operation at the time for which they were planned, might have altered the whole course of the Hitler war.

Fortunately for the Allied nations there was a very long road to be followed before success was achieved. Although experiments with solid propellants had given a reasonable though limited success, the first attempt to use liquid fuel in 1932 ended in disaster. Dornberger describes his feelings as he hid behind a small sapling while the experts put a match to the fuel. He seems to have been anxious. No one was killed or injured, but the test gear was destroyed. Further trials were carried out in the succeeding years but hope alternated with the blackest despair. In 1934, probably as a result of the impatience born of ill-success, a different approach was made to the problem of using liquid propellants with the result that three people were killed. But by December of that year two 4·5″ rockets had been fired successfully, reaching an altitude of 1½ miles. Then followed a long period of trial and error, errors which resulted in many failures. At last, in October 1939, a rocket climbed five miles with complete stability. For this success much credit must go to the young scientist von Braun.

From that time until the 3rd October 1943 when the A4, later called the V2, rose beyond the earth's atmosphere and covered a distance of 125 miles, the story of Peenemünde is

one of steady though unspectacular progress in the face of
constant changes of policy. Hitler had been unconvinced of
the value of the weapon when he visited the experimental
station in March 1939, and in 1940 he had reduced its claims
to a low level of priority, an act for which we in Britain
should be deeply grateful. In the result he may have delayed
the production of the V2 by a matter of months.[1]

The summer of 1942 saw new competition for the resources in manpower and material that were available to the
rocket enthusiasts. According to General Dornberger the
German Air Force started then to develop the V1, which he
calls "a jet-driven air torpedo for catapulting from an inclined
. . . ramp". The G.A.F. had other ideas as well, notably the
radio-controlled gliding bomb that, in 1943, was launched
from an aircraft for the first time against one of our frigates
in the Bay of Biscay. Later this weapon was to sink the Italian
battleship *Roma* on her way to join the Allies. It also caused
losses to our shipping supporting our drive up the Italian coast.

It is interesting to note that, in a more restricted form, our
versatile inventor Sir Denis Burney was advancing theories
on gliding torpedoes, mines and bombs in 1940/41. The
general principle of these weapons was the same as the German
projectile, but they were not radio-controlled. After prolonged
experiment the Air Ministry ruled against the gliding torpedo,
and the mine and bomb were never even given a trial. Some
of us were rather short-sighted in this respect.

Dornberger claims that as early as 1933 he had given his
enthusiastic support to the V1 project, and had financed the
work of an engineer from Munich named Paul Schmidt, who
was developing a pulse motor that powered V1. But, as he
was more than anxious to concentrate his own activities on
the production of the long-range rocket,[2] in the spring of 1940

[1] In spite of this discouragement a form of rocket-propelled bomb
was used against our shipping during the battle for Crete.

[2] The German Navy Department is stated to have been studying the
possibility of producing a gun with a very long barrel in which the
projectile was constantly accelerated down the tube by a succession of
explosions that finally gave it the speed necessary for a very long range.
This gun never came into operation, though preparations for its use
were made at Marquise-Mimoyecques in Northern France in 1943. (*See*
Chap. VII, "The Battle of the Sites".)

he passed the scheme over to Air Staff Engineer Bree of the
G.A.F. Such progress was made by Bree that early in 1943
Hitler ordered a body known as the Long Range Bombardment Commission to decide which of the two weapons, V1
and V2, had the best chance of success. The Commission met
in May at Peenemünde.

Before the comparative tests were carried out in the
presence of Field Marshal ˙Keitel and General Milch the
arguments for and against both weapons were debated in the
mess. The Model Fi 103 (named in other documents as the
PHI 7 or V1) was considerably cheaper than V2. In addition
to its moderate cost it had the advantages of very simple
manipulation, easy transport in ordinary commercial lorries,
and low fuel consumption. These features made operational
mass expenditure possible. The disadvantages were, first, big
fixed launching sites liable to destruction by superior air
power; secondly, the rigid line of fire imposed by the concrete ramps, which would make defence easier; thirdly, the
speed of only 350 m.p.h., and the insufficient height of 600
to 6,000 ft., making the Fi 103 vulnerable to fighters and
medium A.A.; fourthly, the characteristic sound of the engine,
which might warn the enemy. Moreover, the V1 could easily
be detected by radar. Its effect could not exceed that of a
one-ton landmine owing to its low speed of impact.

On the other hand, the A4 rocket could be freely launched
in any direction with little difficulty, and once launched there
was no defence against it or possibility of interference. Dispersion, with proper servicing and testing before firing, was
less than that of the Fi 103. Because of the high speed of impact the effect, if a sensitive proximity fuse were used, would
be greater with the same load of high explosive. The impact
would come as a complete surprise owing to the supersonic
speed. The launching site itself would be difficult or impossible
to identify from the air. Air attack, to be effective, would have
to be restricted to the supply system. Location could be
changed at any time at short notice. The disadvantages, in
addition to higher costs, were vulnerable installations for
testing and supply and the necessity for bomb-proof plants
for liquid oxygen. Moreover, as a result of the high alcohol

consumption and the low supplies of spirit available, output would be fairly low. Finally, in view of the complexity and delicacy of the components of a self-steering rocket, spare parts would have to be available on a rather elaborate scale.

The Commission concluded that the stage of development reached by the two weapons was practically the same. As a result of the "contest" the Commission recommended that both weapons should be put into mass production on the highest priority.

By comparison with this great effort of preparation on Germany's part Britain, as has already been said, had done very little in the development of rocket projectiles. The Air Defence Committee which was set up in 1935 had made recommendations for the provision of a large number of A.A. guns, but by the time war broke out in 1939 the supply of these weapons was woefully inadequate. It was therefore decided to extend the scope of the rocket already developed by further types and these, in a number of forms, were brought into the general scheme of protection against air attack.

The most successful type, though not in the sphere for which it was designed, was that with a 60-pound warhead and with which the Z batteries[1] were equipped. Claims have been made that enemy aircraft were shot down with this weapon, but there seems to be some uncertainty as to their validity. Later, when fired from aircraft at tanks, vehicles, submarines or merchant ships, it proved of outstanding value.

In principle, the War Office had formed the opinion that the rocket, or unrotating projectile, as it was called, would be employed against the dive-bomber, and that no attempt should be made to use it against the high-flying enemy. It had been devised by Dr. Crowe, the scientist responsible for rocket development in Britain, and was propelled by a charge of burning cordite, a point that, as will be seen later, was significant. Service trials of the rocket were being carried out at Aberporth in Wales, and the War Office, in haste to get the weapon into operation, in November 1940 ordered the formation of the first Z or rocket battery. Officers were detailed

[1] The Z batteries were so called because the rockets were on the secret list.

from the Royal Regiment of Artillery, men from the depots, and the Commanding Officer designate was Mr. Duncan Sandys, R.F.A. (T.A.), who at that time held the rank of Major. Sandys' instructions were to take the battery to Malta where the necessary firing trials were to be carried out. Before committing himself to this task he checked on the fitness of his officers for their rôle and found certain changes to be necessary. He then went to Aberporth to obtain the essential briefing in the new weapon. There he found that not only was it still in the early stages of development, but that the supplies available were only sufficient for the needs of Aberporth. Obviously the idea of going to Malta without training and without ammunition was absurd. Major Sandys therefore obtained permission to take his battery to Aberporth where both these necessities could be supplied. Here good progress was made, but still on the lines of the War Office policy. Sandys, however, was not satisfied. Deeply concerned by the damage inflicted on Britain during the winter blitz of 1940, he believed that the rocket was a good weapon to fire against the high-level bomber, if sufficient were fired simultaneously so as to fill the sky in the enemy's vicinity. Having completed his authorized form of training, as well as certain clandestine experiments in high-altitude firing, and being supplied with sufficient ammunition, he moved the battery to the defence of Cardiff. Here, with the aid of a remarkable fire-control table constructed out of Meccano parts, he launched his first attack against the high-flying bomber. Unfortunately, someone must have turned the wrong handle because a hundred or so rockets sped heavenwards but not towards the enemy. A few nights later he had his reward—he claimed a hostile bomber as brought down. Later yet another claim was made and the War Office became converted even to the point of exaggerating the capabilities of the Z batteries. These were promptly created in large numbers. The great advantage of the weapon was its simplicity so that it was found possible to place it in the hands of the Home Guard. It is not recorded whether it had any further successes, but it certainly made a most heartening noise and by its very volume of fire may have discouraged the enemy.

Major Sandys was at one time in command of three of these batteries, two of which were in the line near Cardiff and one doing refresher training at Aberporth. He had to divide his time between the daylight hours of training at Aberporth and the night operations at Cardiff. Rather naturally neither he nor his two drivers got much sleep on their journeys to and fro, and finally one driver drowsed at the wheel and hit a stone wall at high speed. This accident put a stop to Major Sandys' active service and for a period to his association with rockets.

It is now necessary to return to Germany. Few people in Britain can have had any idea of the sense of dedication to a cause that possessed the youth of the Third Reich. Some who travelled in the country in the middle 1930s had the opportunity to see its effects at close quarters. A British business man, intent on selling aero engines to the allegedly civilian German flying clubs, visited an airfield on the Baltic coast. Here he met a number of leading men in the organization, including Herr Heinkel, whom he described as conceited and self-opinionated. Perhaps it was Herr Heinkel's self-sufficiency and confidence that persuaded Goering to make the fatal mistake of believing that the Heinkel 111 was so far superior to the British fighters as to be practically immune from their attacks. For this mistake the British have great cause to be thankful. While conversing with his German opposite numbers the Englishman saw to his surprise, as it was November and bitingly cold, some fifty young Germans, practically naked, emerging from the icy sea and goose-stepping unflinchingly over the pebbly beach. Worse was to follow. The senior member of the German party hailed the leader of the bathing squad and kept him talking for ten minutes, during which time the arctic blast turned the young man from pale pink to alabaster and finally to a congested blue, the whole affair being obviously angled to show the Englishman how tough these products of a rejuvenated Germany could be.

It was this same sense of dedication that drove Dornberger and his team along the dangerous path of rocket development. Colleagues might be killed as the result of risky experiments, large sums of money expended upon apparently fruitless endeavours, but none of these things deterred such ardent souls.

It is difficult to guess what was the prime motive. Was it the urge to travel through space—now described by a leading astronomer as "bilge"—was it that almost religious feeling that leads scientists to carry out research which appears to have no useful purpose whatsoever, or—more likely—was it the military man's desire to make a bigger and better weapon than that possessed by enemy nations?

As Major-General Dornberger is still alive and active in America it would be unfair to attribute any particular motive to him, but it is sufficient to say that as a result of his activities, and those of his colleagues at Peenemünde, Britain and her allies were seriously threatened by a weapon to which at the time there was no reply. So during the 1930s these men worked and risked their lives, while politicians of every hue in Britain strove almost equally hard, but at less personal risk, to preserve "peace in our time".

In France there was not *la noble pourriture* of the grape that produces the quintessence of wine, wine that has, with the courage of her men and the intelligence of her women, been the glory of France through the centuries, but that rottenness, born of the "Front Populaire" which was to bring the French armed forces to ruin. Nothing was being developed of any merit. Socialism run wild suborned and seduced the solid people, and a political system as corrupt as any that has ever scandalized humanity flourished on the rank products of personal selfishness. There were some Englishmen who knew France well enough to realize that in a war with Germany she would, as an ally, be a broken reed. But officially and ambassadorially the façade was maintained that the French Army was of the same quality as that of 1914 (with better armament) and that the Air Force was a worthy companion to the R.A.F. In fact the officer corps had suffered a great loss of morale from the activities of the Popular Front government. Anyone suspected of being an ardent Catholic, or even an efficient officer, ran gravé danger of premature retirement. With this pattern of anxiety and discontent as their daily life it is hardly surprising that the officers, and hence the men, of the French Army and Air Force were not a match for the physically hardened and mentally indoctrinated members of the German armed forces. Further, that while the latter had every encouragement to develop new and exciting techniques of war, the former were well aware that any initiative, especially if it cost money which might be needed for socialist welfare schemes, would be very severely repressed.

Compare this with the attitude of mind of the German people—the Nazis in particular, but a large number of ordinary reasonable people as well. Dornberger speaks of his colleagues at Kummersdorf and Peenemünde as "a team of fanatically inspired and inseparable comrades, linked together for life and death and devoted to one single idea. . . ." It is not surprising therefore that the rotten fabric of French military "power" crumbled at the first onset of armed forces comprising so many men thus dedicated. In England there were also people of the same temper, but under the Government of the day they received very little support in their efforts to build up an answer to Nazi aggression. Nevertheless, mainly along conventional lines—though excluding Radar, a very novel idea—the British fighting machine was gradually developed. Report after report of increasing German armaments forced even the most supine of politicians to agree to greater credits for our armed forces. But no word came about rockets until in November 1939 a series of mysterious communications were received from Germany via Oslo. Today referred to as the Oslo letters, these documents contained a great deal of information about the new weapons with which Hitler intended to win the war. The magnetic anti-shipping mine, radar, the V1 and the V2 were referred to by our informant, who must have been a very highly placed officer in Hitler's hierarchy. If these letters had been taken at their face value, we might have been spared bitter loss. Actually, they were largely disbelieved and only a few imaginative officials worried seriously about them.

As late as January 1940 some of our scientists were convinced that our enemy possessed no radar screen. Practical proof that it did exist was found in the heavy losses to our bomber squadrons that attacked the German warships in Kiel Bay in the autumn of 1939. The magnetic mine, in November 1939, became a most serious menace to our shipping. Fortunately, our scientists produced a method for demagnetizing our ships (known as degaussing) and a fantastic contraption known as the D.W.I. Wellington did yeoman service in the Thames Estuary and later in the Suez Canal. Briefly, this aircraft was equipped with an electrical generating plant which fed current into a large circular electro-magnet that surrounded the fuselage. By flying very low over areas suspected of containing magnetic mines, and with a certain amount of good fortune and grave risk to the crew, the mines could be exploded by the action of this enormous aerial magnet. Naturally, in narrow waters such as the Suez Canal, where the area of search was small, it was more effective than elsewhere. At the same time the Navy developed a magnetic sweeping device which reduced the threat from this type of mine to manageable proportions. But General Dornberger's work on the V2 and that of the G.A.F. on the V1 were not discovered till much later. It needed further proof than the Oslo letters to convince authority that here was a grave risk to our country. Rumours reached Britain from neutral sources, but it was mainly through the reports of our secret agents that a picture began to take shape. These men were working in Denmark, Norway and Sweden, and it was from Denmark that the first definite information about V weapons was received. When it was realized that the first V2 to be fired successfully left the ground in October 1942, and the first V1 in December of the same year, it is an astonishing fact that there was enough information about them available in Britain to enable Major Duncan Sandys to commence his investigation in April 1943. He had been ordered to undertake this task by the War Cabinet, which was still uncertain as to the extent of the threat constituted by the V weapons.

After a month spent in examining the available data and in a series of exciting speculations Major Sandys advised the War Cabinet that the threat was very real and should be taken most seriously.

This recommendation launched the R.A.F. in a major enterprise. The Photo Reconnaissance Unit was given as a first priority task the discovery of the home of the rocket weapons. Evidence pointed strongly to Peenemünde and a wealth of pictures were obtained of this vast organization which had moved from Kummersdorf in 1937 and by 1939 was already absorbing a third of Germany's aerodynamic and technical research resources, having a full-time staff of 12,000 and costing 300 million gold marks

CHAPTER II

PHOTOGRAPHIC RECONNAISSANCE

PHOTO-reconnaissance, as developed between 1912 and 1939, was the lineal descendant of several generations of aerial photographers. In 1858 a French balloonist, Felix Tournachon, photographed a part of Paris, using the daguerrotype process. Two years later an American aeronaut photographed the city of Boston from the air. In 1883 a Major Esdale flew small balloons over New Brunswick in Canada, and from these balloons a camera, presumably operated by a clockwork device, took photographs of the country below.

In the years that followed many pictures were taken from balloons and airships, but these were mainly of use as souvenirs of some individuals' aerial progression.

Since photo-reconnaissance played so large a part in the Allied success in two wars it seems appropriate to set down the incidents of its birth and its development to the present day.

The story of its progress in Britain starts in the years immediately before the Kaiser war, when certain experiments were carried out from R.F.C. Headquarters and from the Royal Aircraft Factory at Farnborough.

The first series of overlapping photographs, that essential factor in air survey, was taken from the airship *Beta* in 1912, by the then Sergeant Laws of the R.E. and R.F.C. This event must be regarded as the birth of photographic reconnaissance from the air. Laws then turned his attention to photography from aeroplanes and, on a ceremonial occasion, stumbled, if such a word can be used in this connection, upon one of the outstanding aspects of his art.

It appears that the Secretary of State for War was reviewing the infant Royal Flying Corps at Farnborough. Laws was determined to photograph the parade as it stood to attention on the grass airfield. As he flew overhead, piloted by Lieut. Fitzjohn Porter, R.A., the inevitable stray dog wandered into the ordered ranks of airmen. This was too much for the sergeant-major, who set off in pursuit. When the resulting photograph was printed the tracks of the dog and of the sergeant-major's ammunition boots were clearly visible on the grass. Thus a second step in air reconnaissance was taken. There is no record of the sergeant-major's capture of the dog, nor of the comments of the airmen on this fascinating episode. But the business of detecting hostile positions by the tracks leading to them had got off to a flying start. Set-backs there were, as when Laws was flying to Netheravon "Concentration Camp" in a Henri Farman piloted by Lieut. Hubbard. Engine failure brought the aircraft down near Odiham and in the ensuing crash the camera was destroyed. The crew escaped with bruises. This was in June 1914, and the "Concentration Camp" was a preliminary to the mobilization of the Royal Flying Corps for the war that lay two months ahead.

Sergeant Laws was, however, not the only air photographer operating at this period. Certain junior officers in the R.F.C. and R.N.A.S. were keen amateur photographers and once they had got over their first enthusiasm for taking pictures of their friends standing by the aircraft in which they proposed to risk their necks, they began to think of aerial photography as one of the new requirements of war.

At first the equipment and technique were very primitive. Cameras designed for picturing landscapes and groups were used from the very draughty cockpits of the contemporary aircraft to photograph forts, harbours, and the training areas of the British Army, such as Salisbury Plain. As is always the case with a new conception, the most wild and wonderful ideas were discussed. One which was not quite so foolish related to the angles at which pictures should be taken at various times of the day, so as to get the maximum "relief" from the available light and shade. Curious diagrams were drawn and patient pilots were afterwards forced to fly in figures of eight over an objective such as Stonehenge while the cameraman endeavoured to prove in practice the theory of the diagrams. While this work was proceeding in the squadrons, the Experimental Flight at Farnborough, under the command of Major Musgrave, R.E., was setting to work in a more scientific manner. It was realized very early on that air photography could be a valuable adjunct to map survey. Thus the photographs required by the surveyors would have to be "verticals" —in fact a photographic map of the ground below. From this need the first cameras were evolved that produced trench and counter-battery maps in the early years of the Kaiser war. The hand-held instrument of 1913/14 soon went by the board, sometimes very practically when the photographer's frozen fingers could not hold it safe in the aircraft's slipstream! Nevertheless, the 'prentice efforts of the Experimental Flight and of the amateurs at Netheravon and Eastchurch had triggered a train of causation that was to produce results of immeasurable importance. In the Kaiser war millions of pictures were taken and reproduced a hundred times each. No Army Commander would move his troops unless he had an up-to-date air map of his operational area. After the war air survey added immensely to our topographical knowledge, and archaeologists were loud in their praise of the success achieved by air photography in revealing the secrets of the past. Again and again misconceptions regarding ancient monuments were corrected by pictures taken from the air, and new knowledge was obtained in the same way.

To return to the process of development. It must be remembered that in 1914/18 the glass plate backed with sensitive emulsion was the main product of the photographic factories. Film was only in its infancy and film packs and rolls were of a very experimental character. The photographic work being carried out at Farnborough was therefore based on the glass plate, and these alone were used in the "period" camera. The business of plate-changing sufficiently rapidly to provide an overlap on each picture, while solvable in the case of an ambling airship such as the *Beta*, was of a different order in aeroplanes flying at least twice as fast.

Obviously a hand-held instrument could not cope, and so for this reason, as well as for several others of a very practical nature, the fixed camera came into being. At first, this was just the old hand-held machine secured to some stable part of the aeroplane. (Vibration of course produced a crop of troubles which springs and sponge-rubber attachments finally

solved.) This contraption came into use in the late autumn of
1914, when trench warfare had produced a demand for maps
of the enemy's defences and of his battery positions. For a
while the relatively short-focus lenses and 5″ × 4″ prints then
available served our needs. But as more detail was demanded
by the Army it became clear that something larger and better
was required. To meet this need Laws, who had joined No. 3
Squadron on mobilization, drew up the specification of the
L-type camera, using a plate 5″ × 4″ and with a lens of 6″ focal
length. This instrument was to serve the Royal Flying Corps
for many months. Meanwhile other developments were
affecting the production of negatives and prints. Before the
outbreak of war the processing of aerial photographs had been
carried out in a box that sat on a tripod and measured about
two feet square. The operator looked through a coloured
screen on the top and watched his hands working in the
relative obscurity of the primitive dark-room. The fastest
time in producing a single print by this method was seventeen
minutes. Clearly something more was necessary under war
conditions. At first more elaborate dark-rooms were established in the cellars of French châteaux, where the bottles of
wine, once they were emptied in a suitable fashion, came in
very handily as containers of developer and hypo. Did an
accident ever occur when hypo was drunk in lieu of hippo-
crene? The seigneur returning after the war to his ravaged
property might well have had this satisfaction.

The first of these improvised dark-rooms was situated near
the small town of Aire. The second was located at Bruay,
near Doullens, under the control of the 3rd Wing, R.F.C.,
whose commander was Lieut.-Colonel J. F. A. Higgins, R.A.
From these small beginnings was built up, through the medium
of mobile processing units, the organization that, as has been
said, was producing by the end of the war hundreds of
thousands of negatives and millions of prints. The first photographic trailer that could be towed from place to place behind
a Leyland lorry was built in the middle of 1915, and to feed
this unit and its brothers, Laws and the Hon. J. T. C. Moore-
Brabazon, who together had joined the 1st Wing R.F.C.,
devised the Laws/Brabazon (L/B) camera fitted with long-

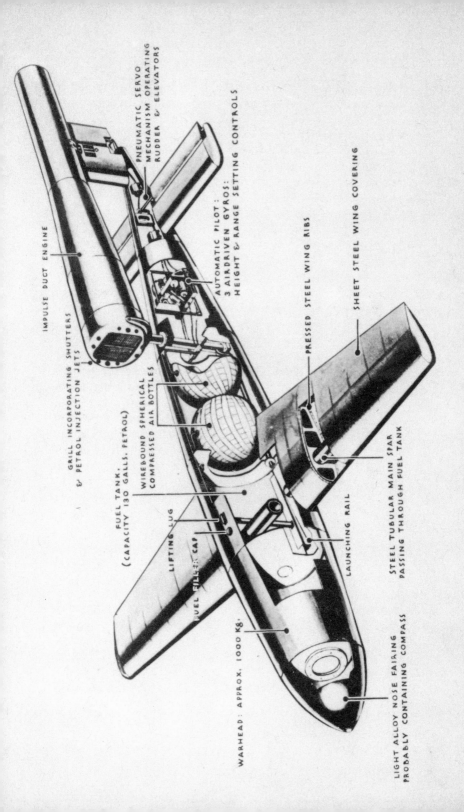

PNEUMATIC SERVO MECHANISM OPERATING RUDDER & ELEVATORS

AUTOMATIC PILOT:
3 AIRDRIVEN GYROS:
HEIGHT & RANGE SETTING CONTROLS

PRESSED STEEL WING RIBS

SHEET STEEL WING COVERING

IMPULSE DUCT ENGINE

GRILL INCORPORATING SHUTTERS
& PETROL INJECTION JETS

WIREBOUND SPHERICAL
COMPRESSED AIR BOTTLES

FUEL TANK.
(CAPACITY 130 GALLS. PETROL)

LIFTING LUG

FUEL FILLER CAP

LAUNCHING RAIL

STEEL TUBULAR MAIN SPAR
PASSING THROUGH FUEL TANK

WARHEAD: APPROX. 1000 KG.

LIGHT ALLOY NOSE FAIRING
PROBABLY CONTAINING COMPASS

Part of Peenemünde Camp before and after the bombardment

focus lenses. As the war progressed the demands of the Army for more detailed information than could be produced by the existing equipment resulted in the construction of the B/M camera, using a plate 7" × 9".

For a while the larger pictures thus produced did satisfy Army requirements, but the size and weight of the new camera was a source of grievance to the pilots and mechanics in the squadrons. By 1918 the Army was asking for more! Fortunately the Armistice and the defeat of Germany put a stop to these apparently insatiable demands. Nevertheless, in the last ten months of the war over ten million prints had been delivered by the mobile units of the photographic branch of the R.F.C. and R.A.F. The negatives from which these prints were produced were obtained by the courage and devotion of the pilots of the Army Co-operation Squadrons and those of the strategical units. Their work was arduous—for example, the Hindenburg Line was frequently photographed from end to end four or five times *a day*. The strategic squadrons penetrated hundreds of miles across the enemy lines to photograph the damage caused to the Rhineland towns by the Independent Bomber Force.

These pictures by themselves would have been valueless without the help of photo interpretation. In the early years of the 1914/18 war the somewhat primitive nature of the cameras used was more than compensated for by the enemy's failure to camouflage important targets. As soon as it was realized how effective was this form of reconnaissance, camouflage became a major activity. As a result the study of photographs became of great importance, and artists expert in form and light and shade were employed to carry out this work. Amongst them was Mr. Solomon J. Solomon, a distinguished painter of the period, who produced a remarkable book of pictures embodying the results of his investigations. So was born the parent of the Photo Interpretation Unit of the Hitler war.

Army Intelligence Officers, wearing the green badge of innocence (a nice touch), were attached to R.F.C. squadrons and were charged with the duty of interpreting the information obtained by air photographs. At first this was a very

C

amateur affair, but before long a mass of material became
available to the General Staff. More and more the work
became specialized. An expert in the clay regions of the Pas
de Calais was at a loss in the chalky valleys of the Somme.
Colour, contrast, light and shade varied from area to area,
and so the technique of interpretation changed from place to
place. But from this study there emerged the volume of knowledge that was to form the basis of air survey in the post-war
years.

One of the most important results of photo-reconnaissance
was the development in Britain of a lens-making and camera-
manufacturing industry. This was of great importance to
national defence. Before 1914 German firms such as Goertz-
Anschutz and Dallmeyer, and Kodak in the U.S.A., held a
practical monopoly of the photographic market. Lumière in
France was a competitor, but a weak one. When the R.F.C.
put forward its war-time requirements to British industry the
consequences of Liberal free trade policy were immediately
apparent. There were only a few small firms fabricating
cameras and the making of special glass for transformation
into lenses was on a derisory scale. In France there was only
one firm capable of making high quality lenses, and the story
goes that British pleas to be shown the necessary technique
were turned down most abruptly. In the end, in spite of the
difficulties of production, the infant industry in Britain produced the answer. By 1918 cameras and lenses were available
to the armed Services on a scale commensurate with the
necessities of the operations then being carried out.

The inconvenience and weight of the photographic plate
had turned the thoughts of designers towards the use of film,
but it was not till after the war that the trick of producing
film that would carry a panchromatic emulsion (essential for
air photography) was learned. The moment this was achieved
the air film camera, lighter and much more convenient than
its predecessor, came into general use. About this time Laws,
who had reached the rank of Squadron-Leader, was posted to
the Directorate of Scientific Research at the Air Ministry, and
here he spent over four years designing new cameras. The first
to be brought into operational use was the F.8, which had

been built and tried out at Biggin Hill. Then the work in connection with its further use was transferred to the Royal Aircraft Establishment at Farnborough. Thirty of these cameras were made, and some were sent to India for test under tropical conditions. The F.8 was not popular with the Air Staff. It was heavy and expensive, and the Staff thought the size of the picture, 9" × 7", too big. The R.A.E. were instructed to produce something smaller and lighter, and finally the F.24, giving a picture 5" × 4", was devised. Laws was certain, however, that neither the focal length nor the picture-size of this camera would satisfy the demands of the future war. He became so dissatisfied with this decision of the Air Staff that he retired and joined a civilian air-survey company. He still kept in touch with the R.A.F., however, and when war broke out he rejoined.

Between the wars photo-reconnaissance, and to an even greater extent photo-interpretation, received very low priority in almost all nations. This type of operation did not tend to attract the more aggressive officers as it was a "dead end", resulting in slow promotion. The use of photo-reconnaissance in a tactical rôle did, however, receive some attention, notably in France and Germany.

Following the reoccupation of the Rhineland by the Germans in 1936, the French started photographing this area quite regularly in order to watch in detail the building of the Siegfried Line. Through this regular photographic cover they were able to see the foundations laid, the walls built, and, finally, the roofs put in place. They took advantage of the great facility which vertical air photographs provide to learn the internal layout of each so-called bunker. Consequently they had a very detailed plan of the whole Siegfried Line.

As a further consequence of doing this work they had, unlike the other allies, a fairly well-developed P.R. unit when war broke out. Its whole emphasis and activity, however, was directed to the Siegfried Line and, perhaps in consequence, they had ignored the wider rôle which P.R./P.I. was destined to play later.

The Germans had been very active in the developing of P.R./P.I. from 1938 onwards. This was largely the result of the work of General von Fritsch, subsequently killed in Poland, who made the rather remarkable statement in 1938 that the country which had the most efficient reconnaissance unit would win the next war. The Germans set out to build a complex P.R./P.I. organization based on independent units with each army. The emphasis, however, was still on military field operations without much reference to air, naval and economic warfare. The organization worked admirably during the rapid advances into Poland, France, and in the early part of the Russian campaign, but was a failure as soon as the war stabilized. It was unable to provide the needed intelligence.

It might well be asked why the Germans, having appreciated the importance of this source so early, failed to modify their methods and techniques to adjust for the changing requirements of the war. There were three main reasons for this, first, that the interpreters, who are the ultimate point at which the value of photographic flying is won or lost, were inferior in quality and given the rank of junior non-commissioned officers. In consequence, if they were any good they were shortly promoted and lost to the task. The second reason was that since the organization was tactical and broken up into small units with each army, there was no cross tie to enable the experience gained in one unit to be transmitted to another, or which linked together information from one front with another front to give a total picture. It is all too true that the value of total information is much greater than the sum of its parts. The third reason lay in the fact that the allies in the west were able to make photographic reconnaissance too costly an operation.

It is perhaps pertinent to interject at this point that the proper extraction and evaluation of air photographs calls for personnel with the highest academic qualifications and who can remain permanently on the job. Interpreters tend to be of little value until they have been on the task for perhaps a year or more. Moreover, the extraction of the maximum information calls for a wide range of specialists who can consult with each other and thus reach solutions on any new activity not previously encountered.

In 1939 the R.A.F. was still thinking in terms of the

1914/18 war. Pictures were to be taken of the enemy front line from slow Army Co-operation aircraft, at heights of up to 17,000 ft.—not more—so that the maximum detail could be shown. Photographs for strategical purposes would be taken from bombers flying at heights of about 20,000 ft. The first weeks of the Hitler war were to bring disillusion.

Into this pleasantly conventional peace-time picture had intruded a rather unusual individual, Mr. Sidney Cotton, and with him other associates. Sidney Cotton was chiefly famous in the Kaiser war for the invention of the Sidcot suit—a warm, windproof, and comfortable covering for the pilots of the Royal Flying Corps, many of whom had suffered agonies from cold while wearing the not-so-imaginative flying kit provided by the Army Ordnance Corps. Cotton was involved in early attempts to fly the Atlantic and to Australia, and in the 1920s carried out some of the first airmail flights in Canada. In the history of Canadian aviation he is credited with being the first man to fly mail to Labrador.

After the First World War he had engaged in a number of activities connected with aviation, but the circumstances that launched him on his air photography career arose from the vicissitudes of the 1931 university expedition to Greenland of which Augustine Courtauld was a leading member. Considerable anxiety was felt in England as to the fate of the expedition and Courtauld's father provided Cotton with a Lockheed monoplane to enable an air search of the ice-cap to be carried out. Before this could be done the expedition returned safely to civilization. Cotton was left in possession of a valuable aircraft of high performance. This he proceeded to put to good use.

Realizing the fact, so often forgotten by military men, that the next war is never like the last one, and being a photographic expert, he proceeded to take pictures, with the equipment then available, from the Lockheed flying at 30,000 ft. But the pictures were lacking in detail and, though he sold a number, his clients were not really satisfied.

In spite of this fact Cotton persisted with his plans. He reckoned that at 30,000 ft. not only would the photo aircraft probably escape ground observation, but even if detected it would be safe from the attention of fighters and A.A. fire. On the outbreak of war he offered his services to the Air Ministry under the name of the "Aircraft Operating Company"—the first of a series of camouflage names for a very "cloak and dagger" organization. Cotton was much encouraged by the support of Air Vice-Marshal Richard Peck, a man of rare intelligence, who, as an amateur photographer of some skill, had fully appreciated what the former was trying to achieve. Peck, at the relevant time, was Director-General of Operations at the Air Ministry and had therefore opportunity to give Cotton the help he required. Cotton not only thought of photography but of its interpretation for military uses. So, alongside the Aircraft Operating Company he developed an interpretation unit, charged with producing the number of photographs required, and also with "reading" them intelligently.

In November 1939 Laws, who had rejoined the R.A.F., was posted to France, and at once decided that the results obtained from the F.24—as used at the time in the aircraft available—were of no value. The thirty F.8 cameras were retrieved from the dusty shelves of the store depots and from India and other places to which they had been sent. Some were fitted to single-seater fighters and immediately began to show their worth. It is interesting to note that Mr. H. B. Stringer[1] of the R.A.E. had fitted F.24 cameras to a Spitfire before the outbreak of war, so the ground had already been broken for the F.8.

In the same month the first P.R. unit, the Heston Special Flight, came into being, equipped with two Spitfires.

On a short period of leave Laws broke all rules by visiting the Deputy Chief of the Air Staff—Air Vice-Marshal Sholto Douglas, himself a rebel and iconoclast—to express his discontent as to the manner in which air photography was being carried out. Sholto Douglas was sympathetic and before long Laws—now a Group Captain—was established in a department of his own creation at the Air Ministry. Here he was under the control of a wise and far-seeing character, Air

---

[1] Later, Hurricanes, Hudsons and Marylands were also fitted with cameras by Mr. Stringer.

Marshal Saundby. This combination achieved remarkable results, and by the spring of 1940 a new instrument, the F.52, using lenses of 36" focal length, was in production. This was the camera that provided the Intelligence Service with information of outstanding value, and in combination with the F.24, used to take oblique pictures, photographed the sites from which V1 and V2 were to be launched against this country. The cameras and lenses themselves were, however, only a part of the necessary organization. In the 1914/18 war, and in the years of peace that followed, the machinery for developing and printing the pictures taken from the air was fairly simple and of modest size. But by 1940 the processing staff were called upon to deal with film nine inches wide and forty or fifty feet long. The developing, fixing, and washing-tanks that were required became very large, and the simple trailers of the Kaiser war could not cope. Laws' initiative had involved the Air Ministry in a construction programme of some magnitude and the administrative machine groaned and creaked under the strain.

Meanwhile, the P.R.U. side of the picture was also making progress. By the beginning of 1940 Air Vice-Marshal Peck achieved a further great advance. At Hendon, No. 212 Squadron, equipped with Spitfires for high-altitude work, and Hudsons for oblique photography, was formed under the command of Wing Commander Tuttle. While this work was proceeding satisfactorily a row had started between Cotton's interpretation organization and the section of the Air Ministry intelligence entitled AI 10 (h). The staffing of this section had not been very well organized and the results obtained from the study of the pictures obtained by the Aircraft Operating Company had been meagre. In sharp contrast were the voluminous reports produced by civilians. In the end the Air Ministry took over the civilians, giving some of the seniors temporary commissions, and from them formed the nucleus of the Photo Interpretation Unit, first at Wembley until a bomb hit the building in which it was housed, and afterwards at Medmenham on the Thames.

No. 212 Squadron worked in France until evacuated in June 1940, almost too late to get away owing to Cotton's insistence that the French would not collapse. As a result of this piece of wishful thinking Cotton was relieved of all further control of operations and P.R.U. became a normal Air Force unit.

One most valuable point emerged from No. 212's work in France. The Squadron needed to cover a very wide front during the German advance and such pictures as it produced gave only very partial information. For example, a bridge would be photographed and shown undamaged. R.A.F. H.Q. would despatch a forlorn hope of Battle aircraft to attack it, though several other bridges, also undamaged and photographed later, were being actively used by the enemy. The principle that "complete cover alone is valuable" thus came to be understood and led to a very much more intelligent and widespread use of P.R. aircraft. Part of the trouble was, of course, due to lack of bomber aircraft.

When France fell and the British forces, having suffered the defeat and disorganization which seems their inevitable fate at the beginning of a war, returned to Britain, No. 212 Squadron found itself as the focus from which developed the considerable organization that was to carry out photographic reconnaissance and interpretation throughout the war. By the middle of 1940 every Government department that was directly connected with the war effort, and very few were not, was clamouring for information from the continent of Europe. Not only was there this vast unsatisfied demand, but the several air force commands were beginning to covet possession of P.R.U. There was a great deal of prestige attached to it as the principal supplier of hot news, but also it was exceedingly useful to whomever directed its activities. The Air Ministry, very wisely, attempted to put an end to these pretensions by forming a P.R. Group, and at first intended to keep it under direct control. This was soon found to be unworkable and so the Group was handed over to a junior organization—Coastal Command. During the course of its existence it was broken up, placed under different commanders, and then re-formed under a single direction.

While there were a number of valid arguments for giving different commands components of the P.R.U., there was one over-riding consideration in favour of its centralization under one headquarters.

A single P.R. aircraft sent over the enemy lines at great height had a very good chance of escaping interception by enemy fighters. The element of surprise was in its favour. But if another similar aircraft was despatched a few minutes later along the same course, the enemy, having been alerted by the first aircraft, would be in a position to intercept its successor. Obviously then it was necessary that the general pattern of P.R. sorties should be woven by one authority, which would naturally take the greatest care not to provoke a situation where the loss of man and machine might be incurred. Co-ordination from the Ministry was not enough. It was tried and found wanting. Thus the centralized command had to be established, and this continued to the end of the war.

As P.R.U. became firmly established its equipment improved. In fact, it became the established practice of the Air Staff to provide P.R.U. with the very latest models of fighter aircraft as these came into operation. This procedure led to a very early conflict between the needs of air reconnaissance and of radar-controlled night fighting. The Mosquito two-seater fighter was very suitable for both rôles, but P.R.U. won the battle of priorities at a time when the night bombardment of London had become a real threat.

With the improvements in equipment the range of operations was extended. Mosquitos searched the coasts of Norway for Atlantic raiders, operating sometimes from Russian airfields in the Archangel area. Factories in Czecho-Slovakia were visited and from Malta and the North African coast daily sorties watched for Rommel's supply ships. From India the Japanese-held territories of Burma and Sumatra were kept under observation, and periodical visits were paid to the Andaman Islands to see that the enemy fleet was not concentrating there for a raid on our communications in the Indian Ocean. The battleship *Tirpitz* anchored in Trondheim harbour was the source of trouble to P.R.U. aircraft. So much so that at Christmas 1942 the squadron based on Leuchars in Scotland devised a greetings card of some significance. This card showed a lonely Spitfire flying above a gloomy fiord surrounded by cloud-capped hills. The caption read "Never have so many gone so far for so little".

The *Scharnhorst* and *Gneisenau* in Brest harbour were the subject of even greater endeavour. Reconnaissances were made on every flyable day to establish the continued residence of these ships in an anchorage that was made exceedingly uncomfortable for them by the periodical attentions of Bomber Command.

One task achieved by P.R.U. was to establish beyond doubt that our early night raids on Germany were achieving very little success. Our bomber crews quite genuinely believed that they had hit their targets, but when these were photographed by the "damage assessment" aircraft very little could be seen. At first "Bomber" Harris blamed the cameras, claiming that the pictures they took did not show the damage which must have existed. Scientific analysis of the pictures and of the crew reports showed conclusively that most of the bombers' efforts were wasted in open spaces some distance from the objectives. As soon as radar aids to navigation and the Pathfinder target-marking technique were developed towards the end of 1942, "damage assessment" pictures taken in 1943 told a very different story.

The Americans had been watching the activities of P.R.U. with great interest, and even before Pearl Harbour had taken steps to develop a similar organization. They were helped by the fact that certain U.S. aircraft, for example the Maryland light bomber, had been used by us in the P.R. rôle. By the time the United States was in the war the U.S.A.F. was able to assist the British in a big way.

P.I.U. had grown in size and scope parallel with P.R.U. Its establishment had soon outgrown the facilities at Wembley, which it first used, and a move was made to Medmenham, where the buildings in and around Phyllis Court afforded room and scope for further expansion. It enjoyed no startling development in its work and such improvements that took place were mainly in the experience and increasing skill of the personnel of the Unit. When America entered the war it was renamed the "Allied Central Interpretation Unit" and was to some extent placed under the control of the joint Chiefs of

Staff. Manning was carried out by personnel of all the Allies and all services. This system ensured a scheme of priorities that worked reasonably well.

The history of P.R.U. and P.I.U. is thus brought to the point where air photography and interpretation became major factors in the battle against the "V" weapons, the *Vergeltungswaffen* that were to revenge the Germans for Britain's entry into the war and for the defeat of Goering's bombers.

CHAPTER III

HITLER AND THE REVENGE WEAPONS

IT is interesting to think that Hitler himself was responsible
for some of the delay in developing V1 and V2. He visited
Kummersdorf in 1933 and had not been impressed by the
makeshift organization that was struggling to survive in the
face of lack of funds and inadequate facilities. He was also
upset by the wild talk of the "space travellers" such as von
Braun, one of Dornberger's staff, and even the latter's ex-
planations of the work going on were unconvincing as
experiment after experiment failed for lack of full preparation
and over-enthusiastic anticipation. The mind of the "Corporal"
—at least at that time—was mainly concerned with aircraft,
tanks, submarines and vast armies with which he was going
to blast his way to world domination. So he gave no support
to the project. Fortunately for Dornberger, a succession of
Chiefs of Staff—Fritsch to a certain extent and von Brauchitsch
wholeheartedly—continued to believe that here was a world-
beating weapon. From 1936 onwards good progress was made
at Kummersdorf and later at Peenemünde, but the war was
only a month old when Hitler discovered what was going on.
In his view that was not the moment to spend money, materials
and manpower on a weapon which, so far as he was concerned,
was a figment of the imagination of a collection of mad pseudo-
scientists. So Peenemünde went to the bottom of the priority list
and only just enough was saved by von Brauchitsch's influence to
enable research to proceed, though on a markedly reduced scale.

The relative failure of the bombers of the Luftwaffe during
the Battle of Britain added strength to von Brauchitsch's
arguments. However, his suggestion that V2 should now be
given priority as a successor to Goering's bombers was ill
received by Hitler, who was already planning his attack on
Russia. The needs of the projected campaign in terms of conventional weapons made it imperative that all effort should
be conserved, and so the rocket programme remained at a low

44

priority. To von Brauchitsch must be given the credit that in spite of Hitler's orders he despatched to Dornberger a considerable force of engineers on his own authority. As a result of this prescient action Dornberger was able to launch the first successful V2 on the 3rd October 1942, from the experimental firing range at Peenemünde.

It is necessary to repeat at this stage that Hitler's vacillations had set back the production of V2 by a period of time which the lack of full details of production schedules and provision of material make it impossible to assess with any accuracy, but must have amounted to many months. This, however, was not the end of Dornberger's troubles. He was yet to meet a railway-engine production manager with the charming name of Degenkolb.

Degenkolb's claim to the favour of Speer, the equivalent in Germany of our Minister of Production, was that by employing the most ruthless methods he had increased very largely the number of locomotives needed by the German Army. Speer considered him the man to increase the production of V1 and V2 to the point where Hitler's desire to launch a thousand, even five thousand, of each of these weapons every 24 hours against Britain might be achieved.

According to Dornberger this was to attempt the impossible. Neither weapon was in a fit state of development to be put into production on this scale in time for the proposed attack in December 1943. There was also something rather sinister in Degenkolb's plan to turn Peenemünde into a limited liability company. How this action could improve matters was far from clear. What was certain, however, was the arrival of a number of Degenkolb's friends to fill lucrative and important posts in the existing organization. The consequent wrangling and jealous manœuvring added greatly to Dornberger's troubles and must have produced further delays in the development of the weapons.

Meanwhile V2 had achieved success and its triumphant launching had been the occasion of almost hysterical joy at Peenemünde. It is a pleasant reflection on General Dornberger's character that he was the first to give credit to the man whose original ideas had launched the project.

According to Joseph Warner Angell, writing in an American magazine and with apparently first-hand information from Dornberger himself, the latter used the following words in proposing Dr. Oberth's health at the inevitable drink party: "This modest, unworldly scientist . . . this restless mind, concealing a superabundance of ideas, with his fanatic faith in an era of rockets and space travel. Accept, senior master and father of so many ideas, my heartiest congratulations!" What a change from the jostling of scientists and inventors, even of Service leaders in other countries, in their endeavour to establish their priority in a claim to fame!

To do Hitler justice, after his earlier attitude of hostility to the V2, he began to change his mind in the spring of 1942 and sent for Dornberger and von Braun from his H.Q. on the Eastern Front. At this meeting Dornberger gave the Führer an outline of his requirements in men and material at Peenemünde and his need for launching sites in Northern France. To these proposals Hitler agreed, but at the same time encouraged the Luftwaffe to press on with its experiments with V1.

The programme then appeared to be well launched and Dornberger considered that he could open his attack on London about the middle of 1943. One more halt was, however, to be called by Hitler himself. In the early spring of 1943 it appears that he dreamt the V2 would never land in England and, "depending upon my inspiration", he gave orders that the production of V2 should cease. Thanks, however, to the intervention of Speer, Hitler changed his mind again, though now the date of the attack on London was given as January 1944.

CHAPTER IV

THE SANDYS INVESTIGATION

IT was obvious to General Dornberger that the work at Peenemünde over such a period of years could not remain completely secret. In fact, Peenemünde and its weapons had figured in the Oslo letters, and from Sweden, Denmark, and later from Poland came scrappy reports of something sinister brewing in the many buildings that had been erected among its pine trees and on its sandy beaches.

In Denmark there were many brave people who were very disinclined to accept German aggression, and of these not the least distinguished was V. L. U. Glyth, now a Colonel in the Danish Army and at present attached to the Danish Royal Family at Christiansborg Palace. It was Glyth, then a Major in the Intelligence Service, who, as the British diplomatic train drew out from Copenhagen after the German invasion had started, threw a parcel containing the latest intelligence of the enemy's movements into the guard's van. It was Glyth who, with his chief, Colonel Nordentoft, continued to work for the Allies during the German occupation of Denmark. At first the pressure of this occupation was light and, apart from supervision at the upper levels, the Danish Naval and Army Intelligence system continued to function, ostensibly only for internal purposes, but actually on behalf of the Allies. An intelligence network, composed of the ship masters and seamen of the Baltic coastal traffic, had been set up early in 1940 and thus fulfilled the functions for which it had been designed.

From time to time came messages, whispered to contacts in quayside cafés, that there were queer goings on in the Western Baltic. The name of Peenemünde figured in these reports, but for many months nothing definite became known. However, in the files of Danish Intelligence a mass of uncorrelated reports began to accumulate. Then came some startling statements from Danish fishermen working in the vicinity of Bornholm Island. Strange aeroplanes had been seen which at night had a flaming tail. They seemed to come from the direction of Peenemünde.

By the middle of 1942 reliable clandestine wireless communication had been established between Denmark and London, and these reports were made available to the British, who had already some indication of what was going on through the medium of the Oslo letters. In the winter of 1942/43 more and more information became available, pointing to some sort of rocket-projectile development at Peenemünde. London was most interested and the Danes were urged in July 1943 to do everything possible to discover what was happening. From the information already obtained Glyth was able to prepare an appreciation of what this aircraft might be and, though at the time his report appeared fantastic, even to himself, it was very near the truth about the "V" weapons.

Within a few days, on 22nd August, to be exact, another startling event occurred. One of the "aeroplanes with flaming tails" crash-landed on the island of Bornholm. This information was telephoned from the place of landing by a police-sergeant called Pedersen from his station at the village of Nexö to J. Hansen, the police superintendent at Rönne. Hansen's report is as follows:

"Sunday, 22nd August 1943, Rönne.

At 13.05 hours on August 22nd 1943, Police Sergeant Pedersen at the Police Station at Nexö received a telephone report to the effect that an aircraft had crashed at Bodilsker. No further information could be provided and P.S. Pedersen transmitted the report to me in the form in which he had received it. Pedersen at once drove to the place to cordon it off and to take such steps as might be necessary.

Having advised the German Command on the island, I drove to the place accompanied by Lieutenant Commander Christiansen, and arrived at about 14.15 hours. The Lieutenant Commander is C.O. of the Naval District of Bornholm and accompanied me partly in his capacity as Liaison Officer and partly as Mine Disposal Officer. The German 'Wehrmacht' arrived at the place at about 14.30 hours.

The aircraft had been flying in direction SSW-NNE

Wing-Commander
I. H. Searby, D.F.C.

Peenemünde living
quarters after
the bombardment

British defence against V1. A vast concentration of aircraft, guns and searchlights

and it crashed about 2 km WNW of Bodilsker Church. Information obtained from the local inhabitants was to the effect that the aircraft came at great speed and gave a loud whistling sound during its flight. It was flying at low altitude at some distance from the place where it crashed, having barely missed the tops of the trees around a house only 250 metres away."

Then follows a description of the construction of the missile, and its contents which were visible owing to its disintegration in the crash. This information is given in great detail, pointing to a considerable knowledge of engineering and electronics on Hansen's part.

Hansen then continues:

"The representatives of the German 'Wehrmacht' (a lieutenant of the Navy, the adjutant) and a 'Feldwebel' of the 'Luftwaffe') shook their heads when they saw the apparatus and declared that they had no idea what it was. They stated, however, that it was of German manufacture and it was therefore carted to 'Wehrmacht' headquarters at Rönne. It filled a large lorry.

In many places the machine bore the legend V¹-83 painted in black and a metal plate riveted to a valve carried the inscription 'BAUART' followed by several figures.

There was not time for a more detailed examination and description since the German representatives arrived about fifteen minutes after ourselves.

It is impossible with any amount of certainty to make a statement of the nature of the object. It may well be remotely controlled, its dimensions in proportion to its weight being much too small to make it possible to use it as a glider, nor were any aircraft heard in the neighbourhood at the time in question.

I noticed a container in the body of the machine which seemed to be made of too thin metal to contain compressed air in any quantity, and I am therefore inclined to believe that the propellant used has been some combustible gas or liquid, and that the apparatus has been propelled on the rocket principle.

The concrete forepart weighing about 150 kg. would

D

seem to indicate that it is a question of a remote-controlled training bomb in which the explosive charge has been replaced by concrete."

Lieutenant-Commander Christiansen takes up the story:

"On August 22nd 1943 a German long-range rocket crashed on the island of Bornholm. The rocket was photographed and in the evening of that day I forwarded to the Ministry of Marine a report and drawing. On August 23rd I further forwarded four different photographs of the rocket, all to be used as decided by the Intelligence Section of the Naval Staff. On the part of the Germans I was asked whether the rocket had been photographed. This question was, of course, answered in the negative."

These photographs and the report were forwarded to Colonel Glyth by Christiansen through his chief, Commander X——. Three copies of the pictures and reports were sent to London through different channels. Unfortunately, one messenger, a sailor working on the Elsinor-Helsingborg (Sweden) ferry, was detected and the report seized by the Germans. Christiansen continues:

"During the night of August 29th/30th the events occurred which led to the scuttling or flight to Sweden of the fleet, and the internment of army and navy personnel etc. My position as Naval District Officer on Bornholm for about three and a half years had in course of time led to my being used as local Liaison Officer between the Danish Authorities and the German officer in command, so as conditions were on Bornholm, I considered it my duty to remain in my post pending further orders.

On September 1st, a Major of the 'Luftwaffe' asked for a statement concerning the finding of the rocket and showed me an enlargement of one of the photographs. How the Germans obtained an enlarged copy of one of the photographs has not been fully clarified.

My interview with the Major was, however, interrupted by a report of a mine at the 'Hammer' harbour. In continuation of my previous work as Mine Disposal Officer I considered it my duty to render the mine harmless.

On completion of my work on the mine it had—as conditions had developed—been my intention to proceed to Sweden in my Mine Disposal Craft, but this proved impracticable as two German vessels were lying close by keeping my craft under observation.

Shortly after my return to Rönne I was interned. On September 5th I was transferred to Copenhagen and interned at the Naval Dockyard. A few days later I was taken out for examination by the Germans. An inspector of the German Criminal Police was in charge of the examination which was attended by a Major of the Luftwaffe.

I was informed that it was an extremely serious matter and that only by telling the full truth I might expect a reasonable outcome. They further advised that they were in possession of proof that my photographs and reports had been sent out of the country, and wanted me to explain why I had previously denied that the photographs had been taken. Concerning the photographs I made a statement that could neither be proved nor disproved. Otherwise I maintained that I had acted solely in my official capacity. In reply to a question concerning my reports I informed them where some of the reports were to be found, knowing that this could not hurt anybody else, and believing that it might benefit my cause. Finally, they informed me that an investigation would now be made on Bornholm and that in due course I should hear further from them.

After the examination I returned to the Naval Dockyard where the negotiations concerning my status gave rise to sundry misunderstandings, so that the upshot was that I was admitted to the Municipal Hospital of Copenhagen. This was contrary to my own plans as a civilian worker in the Dockyard had promised to help me to escape disguised as a workman.

At the Municipal Hospital one of the ward doctors offered to get me out, but as the preparations would take a couple of days he gave me an injection which gave me a high fever, so that I might be really ill if in the meantime the Germans were to call for me. Next day I was visited by two friends who came to help me to escape. At the same time I was, however, informed by the Ministry of Marine that I should remain where I was, and that they would get me out in case of necessity. The reason was that at that time the Ministry of Marine considered it possible to have the case against me dropped so that, like many other Danish officers, I would only be interned for the duration. Admiral Vedel had personaly carried on negotiations to that effect. I therefore decided to bide my time.

On September 13th two Danish C.I.D. Officers called and demanded that I be handed over to them. When I had almost finished dressing the Gestapo arrived, however, and took me to the 'Vestre Fængsel' (Western Prison) so that the planned *Danish* action to get me out of German power miscarried. On the way to the prison I was at the Frederiksberg Hospital examined by a German physician who declared that there was nothing the matter with me. On the whole I was rather roughly treated—I was told that I was a damned spy, and that it would not be many days before I had confessed everything. To wind up with, they asked me whether I wanted to take leave of my wife.

During the same night—September 13th—I was subjected to a very lengthy German examination. In reply to a question put by me I was informed that I was charged with espionage, and that I had once deceived them so if I did not speak the truth now it would be all up with me. Some of my reports which, according to them, had not been sent direct to the Ministry of Marine, were pure and simple espionage. I was further charged with having removed German military documents and secretly carried them to Copenhagen. Finally, they tried to convict me of having collaborated with the Intelligence Section of the Army General Staff, and of having received payment for my work. I persisted in maintaining that I had only been doing my official duty but it was, of course, difficult to get away from the fact that the Germans were in possession of one of my photographs, and that they knew that one set of pictures was missing in their account of the total number of copies made.

Next day I was again examined by the Germans and finally a written report of my statements was placed before me for signature. Many statements seemed to me to have been distorted, and with great difficulty I induced them to change one important matter—namely a statement to the effect that the removal of German military objects (magnetic mines etc.) from Bornholm, had been done 'unofficially', it being admitted that such objects had by me been transported to the Ministry of Marine (the Naval Dockyard).

It is not clear to me what happened after that examination as a period of about six days is entirely missing from my memory. I did not regain consciousness until September 20th or 21st, when I found myself in a basement cell in the German ward of the Frederiksberg Hospital. I was sore all over and had pains when I tried to move. Besides I had two wounds on my shins, one on the hip, and bruises all over my body.

On September 22nd I was taken back to the Western Prison, but this time to another division. What happened from that date and until October 8th is very hazy to me. Now and then I was subjected to short examinations and asked whether I had anything further to add. I am aware, however, that I answered this in the negative. I remember that on several occasions I vainly protested against being taken for walks in the yard as I had difficulty in getting up and down stairs due to pain. Likewise, it was almost impossible for me to scrub the floor of my cell as it was very painful for me to bend over.

Despite my wounds and bruises I do not remember that on any occasion I was exposed to physical violence. I am convinced, however, that I have in different ways been exposed to violent physical pressure which made my nerves fail to such an extent as to make it impossible for me to estimate exactly what I was exposed to during a protracted period of my stay in prison.

From the prison I was taken to the Municipal Hospital on October 8th. On October 22nd, six unknown men called for me. I arranged with the leader of the group that he should make it look as if I had been forcibly removed in order that no one should get into difficulties. During my stay 'underground' in Copenhagen, a doctor attended to my wounds. On October 26th I was 'illegally' removed to Sweden, and, according to a request from the Ministry of Marine, the Royal Danish Legation at Stockholm then took charge of my affairs.

On October 30th I got severe pains in my hip and a bad fever. I was then admitted to the Municipal Hospital of Malmö.

On November 23rd I left the hospital and received

out-patient treatment until November 30th, when I left
for Delarne for reconvalescence.

On December 3rd heavy pains in my hip recurred.
When I applied to the local Hospital at Säter I was informed
that an operation would be necessary, and this operation
was performed the next day. After the operation the
doctor told me that a major operation would be required,
and as they could not keep me at their hospital I was
transferred to the Avesta Hospital.

On December 23rd the surgeon told me that it would
probably take some months for the wound to heal, and
that I might just as well be treated at home by the local
practitioner.

By the beginning of March 1944 the wound had healed
and I then at once reported for service with the 'Command
of Danish military Refugees' which organized the training
and service of army and navy personnel and volunteers
who due to the prevailing conditions were temporarily
staying in Sweden.

(signed) Chr. H. Christiansen."

Christiansen's connection with X—— and Glyth was clear
and the Danish police immediately warned these two officers
and their chief, Colonel Nordentoft, that the Gestapo were
after them. While the others might have hid successfully
Glyth was easily identifiable by a facial scar. So the three of
them and X——'s secretary, Miss Y——, who was equally
implicated, slipped on to a fishing-boat at seven-thirty on an
evening in late August 1943 and set course for Sweden. They
were within two or three miles of the neutral coast when
German patrol-boats appeared. Quickly stripping cork floats
from a fishing-net, they made themselves primitive lifebelts
and, slipping over the side, they started to paddle for the
shore. Fortunately the German patrol-boats saw no signs of
their hasty exit and the fishermen escaped with a severe
reprimand for fishing too near the Swedish coast. Icy cold and
very frightened, the swimming party pressed on and finally
reached the island of Hven—and safety.

The Swedes were more than helpful. A boat came over at
once from the mainland and soon the party, still dripping wet
from their swim, were in the night train for Stockholm. Miss

Y—— tells an amusing story of how she, in jumper and slacks, with her hair hanging draggle-tailed down her back, was given a bunk in a sleeping compartment with a very elegant Swedish lady who was completely horrified at the intrusion. This person's feelings when Miss Y—— was met on Stockholm station platform the following morning by a very smart Swedish officer detailed from the War Office and carrying a bunch of two dozen beautiful red roses can well be imagined. The officer could not have been completely disappointed in his mission because, no doubt, his visitor had carried out running repairs in the train and there is ample evidence of her good looks and charm of manner. The men of the party appeared in denim overalls and bedroom slippers.

Nordentoft, X—— and Miss Y—— remained in Sweden organizing the refugees from Denmark that were coming over in a steady stream. Glyth, about four weeks after his escape, flew over to Leuchars in the Mosquito service that plied between Stockholm and the United Kingdom. His journey, at great height, in the bomb bay of the Mosquito, must have been at least as uncomfortable as the swim in the waters of the Sound.

·   ·   ·   ·   ·

In the story of the Polish Air Force, *Destiny Can Wait*, is a vivid, factual account of how the Polish Underground movement worked for weeks and months to resolve the problem of the German revenge weapons. In 1941 a drunken German airman boasted to a Polish member of the Underground in Königsberg that there was a new weapon with which Germany was to conquer the world. Engineer Bree must have chosen his staff without due care.

This information was passed to Warsaw, where it evoked no interest beyond its reference to a Mr. A. Kocjan, engineer and aircraft designer. Kocjan was receptive and gave instructions that the information was to be followed up. Unfortunately nothing further transpired until early in 1943, when Kocjan learned that some new weapon was being tried out by the Luftwaffe at Peenemünde. London was immediately informed and a request was received by the Staff of the Polish

Home Army Intelligence that an exact map of this new station
should be obtained. A number of devoted Poles were despatched to carry out this mission, which they achieved successfully. In addition, some Polish slave-workers who had
been detailed by the Germans for duty in Germany were told
to keep their eyes open and report, through the Underground
service, anything of importance that they observed. At least
two of these workers arrived at Peenemünde, and were shortly
ordered, since they were intelligent and educated, to carry out
latrine fatigue inside the secret part of the camp. As cleaners-
out of buckets and collectors of waste-paper they could wander
throughout the buildings without question. During these
wanderings they gathered some information, but days were
to pass before anything of importance was seen. Then, passing
by a shed where the door had been left open, one of them saw
a torpedo-shaped object fitted with wings. It might be a small
aeroplane, but where would the pilot sit? It was much too
small. Doubtfully the information was passed to Warsaw,
where a scientist closely associated with the Underground saw
its significance. Almost immediately afterwards a Polish
engine-driver, working trains between Bromberg and Warsaw,
reported that his son, a slave-worker, had been for a year in
a camp where secret weapons were being developed. The
name of the camp was Peenemünde, and what he had seen
there confirmed the latrine orderly's story.

Other evidence from secret sources pointed to the Opel
works at Russelsheim as a source of rocketry. In March 1943
a captured German general (his name must be withheld in his
own interest) mentioned that he had seen rockets which were
supposed to win the war for Germany. He had not been impressed by their performance, in spite of the fervid advocacy
of the officers in charge of their development. It was this
statement, confirmed by another German general who is not
named in the records, that was the turning-point in the attitude
of Intelligence to the rocket threat. At last the picture outlined
in a paper by a young scientist attached to the Air Ministry
Intelligence, written in January 1943, and which was based on
reports received in the previous two years, came clearly into
focus.

London was very pleased! Thus we arrived at the point where the combination of the Oslo letters, the reports from Denmark and Sweden and, finally, the confirmation of these pieces of the jigsaw puzzle by prisoners, and the news from Poland enabled the War Cabinet to take action. The volume of evidence that something very important was happening grew to a point where the Chiefs of Staff, mindful no doubt of Major Sandys' previous association with rockets, decided to invite him to conduct a special investigation into the problem presented to the Allies by this new threat from Germany. With the letter issuing the invitation came a few scraps of paper containing the information which had so disturbed the Chiefs of Staff. This was in April 1943.

Major Sandys got to work at once, and P.R.U.[1] departed on the many missions which were to infuriate the Air Staff by their apparent uselessness and to puzzle the pilots as to their necessity. Gradually a pattern began to show itself. Though the buildings at Peenemünde were in no sense remarkable, yet among them were certain structures resembling gun emplacements. But instead of being above ground these were sunk, and though they might have been thought of as part of the coast defences, they did not follow the coastline. They were exactly parallel to one another and pointed in a direction which, if extended, went inland but, more significantly, out to sea, avoiding the many islands that fringe the South Baltic coast. Finally at the same spot in each of these emplacements there was a dark patch—as though the ground had been scorched. It seemed, therefore, as though some unknown weapon giving off very high temperatures was being fired over the sea from these sites.

Reconnaissance was intensified and finally on the 18th June 1943 a picture showed a number of long cylindrical objects in an emplacement, and near by an obvious lifting device. Towards the shoreline a vertical object, thought to be a large pole, was also apparent, but as it was away from the emplacement the

---

[1] Peenemünde had been photographed by P.R.U. in May 1942, and in January, February and March 1943, without any startling results, though the January flight was made on the advice of A.P.I.U. that the place might be connected with rocket development.

significance of its presence there was not obvious. From all this Sandys deduced that the weapon was a very long-range rocket, and that a heavy air attack should be delivered at Peenemünde. When appealed to for his opinion Lord Cherwell, scientific adviser to the Prime Minister, expressed his disbelief in this theory. In his view the rockets, if indeed the objects seen were rockets, and not some form of balloon, were no danger to us. Faced with these conflicting views the War Cabinet, supported by the Air Staff, refused to sanction the attack. Undefeated, Sandys summoned to his aid a panel of the country's leading scientists and placed the evidence before them. They consulted Dr. Crowe, the chief rocket expert of the Ministry of Supply. Crowe assumed that German rockets, like the small British A.A. rockets he had developed, must burn the usual solid propellent—cordite. He argued that to get the necessary thrust the charge would have to be burned in a large steel container. The heat engendered by this over the period necessary to carry the rocket to its target many miles away would be so intense that the container would have to be immensely strong and immensely heavy. By the process of *reductio ad absurdum* he proved that by no manner of means could such a rocket travel the distance required. Convinced by this expert advice which was based on a reasonable, though unfortunately erroneous, assumption, the panel gave Sandys no support. Nevertheless, Sandys persisted in advancing the view that dangerous weapons were being developed at Peenemünde and that a vigorous attack should be delivered against this place. His views were placed before the War Cabinet at the end of June 1943 and the next day this body issued its decisions. Peenemünde was to be most heavily bombed at the earliest possible date. With some hesitation, since as late as the 26th June the Assistant Chief of the Air Staff had again expressed his doubts to Sandys, the Air Staff gave the necessary orders.

Bomber Command Headquarters were anxious. Peenemünde was much farther away from our bases than the targets that were being attacked at the time, and the existing navigational aids would be inoperative at that range. In consequence of this latter fact the attack would have to be made in bright moonlight, to be sure of identifying the target, and so with grave danger from the enemy night-fighters. When the method of attack came up for consideration, it was originally proposed to employ three waves of aircraft, each covering the whole of the target area. However, it was pointed out that the crux of the rocket development lay in the minds of the scientists living in the "settlement". If they were not caught unawares in the first attack they would get into shelters and trenches before the second and third waves delivered their bombs. The permanent installations, workshops, fuel stores, and launching gear could not run away and could just as well be attacked subsequently. So the plan of attack was made.

CHAPTER V

THE ATTACK ON PEENEMÜNDE

IT must be emphasized that the operations against the revenge weapons fell into two distinct categories: the first being the attacks on Peenemünde and on the factories that supplied the fuel and parts for V1 and V2, and the second being the discovery and destruction of the launching sites, storage places and supply centres in N.-W. Europe. The decision of the Defence Committee embodied both these projects in one statement.

". . . the most searching and rigorous examination of the area in Northern France within a radius of 130 miles from London should be organized and maintained, no step being neglected to make this as efficient and thorough as possible. The attack on the experimental station at Peenemünde should take the form of the heaviest possible night attack by Bomber Command on the first occasion when conditions are suitable. That as far as possible plans should be prepared for immediate air attack on rocket firing points in Northern France as soon as these are located."[1]

Thus P.R.U., already heavily loaded by the demands of the three Services for photographic intelligence relating to the bomber offensive, the plans for the invasion of France, the operations in the Mediterranean and the war at sea, was given a further task of great scope. Fortunately by this time the resources available in pilots and aircraft were beginning to measure up to these demands, and in the ensuing months a vast amount of photographic cover as well as the results of visual reconnaissance were made available to the intelligence departments. Of these it could no longer be said that "never has so little been known about so much by so many"! Indeed, these operations became so fruitful that the enemy began to see spies in every hedgerow and under each conference table.

[1] Sir Winston Churchill, *The Second World War*, vol. v, p. 204.

The next problem was to deal with the home of the V1 and V2. So Bomber Command addressed itself to the destruction of the many acres of varied installations that composed the rocket and flying-bomb development organization at Peenemünde. Air photographs had given a very good indication of the extent of this place, and its situation on the sea-coast near the conspicuous island of Rugen made it an easy target to find.

There were also the factories making components or the fuel for the rockets—the I. G. Farben establishments at Leuna, Oppau, Ludwigshafen and Fredrickshafen—widely separated units. These were to be dealt with later.

Before Peenemünde was attacked, however, Bomber Command decided to try out a plan that had been considered some time previously. Throughout the early days of the bomber offensive from 1940 onwards there had been great disappointment at the relatively poor results obtained from night attacks on targets in Germany. Bad weather, cloud, haze, smoke and darkness had all made their contribution to this failure.

In 1941 night photographs taken by aircraft of our bomber force and the day pictures produced by the Photo Reconnaissance Unit had shown most clearly that our bombs were not hitting their target. A Professor Dickens made a most able analysis of the story told by these photographs, and it made very sad reading. Aircraft were being destroyed and valuable lives lost without any commensurate injury to the Germans. For some months discussions proceeded without any important results being achieved. Gradually, however, it was borne upon Bomber Command Headquarters that some definite action, beyond the normal improvements in crew training, would be required before the enemy would be hit hard enough to matter.

At first the solution seemed to rest with improved aids to navigation. Radio aids were therefore developed, in addition to the wireless beacons that gave the bombers a good start from our shores.

The first of these was known as "Gee". This mechanism could give an accuracy of some two miles in width and four to six miles in length on a target over 200 miles from base. "H" was a parallel design that gave greater dispersion in width but more accuracy in range. At the same time "Oboe", a very much more accurate system with a range of 240 miles, took its place in the programme. All three of these systems, however, depended upon ground stations in Britain and consequently their range was limited. A much more refined device that did not suffer from range limitations, since it was carried in the aircraft itself, was "H_2S". This instrument became available as the result of the development of centimetric "Radar", and it gave a telephoto picture of the ground under the aircraft in which it was installed. This picture could differentiate between land, sea and buildings, and so was particularly successful in "seeing" towns on rivers or on the seashore. By using one or all of these methods Bomber Command greatly improved the accuracy of its attack. But two further developments had been found necessary.

In the Royal Air Force in 1939/40 was a very dynamic personality called Don Bennett.[1] This officer, after some rather hectic experiences during the Norwegian campaign, turned up in the office of the C.-in-C. Coastal Command, some time in 1941. He had certain proposals to make, but the C.-in-C., having come to the conclusion that if Bennett joined his command it would not be long before he would have to resign his post in favour of the latter, gave him no encouragement. Bennett then joined Bomber Command and was to some extent responsible for a development which was to have a most important influence on the functions of our bomber force. He was quick to realize that the failure of our bombers to hit their targets was not due, as our medical men were inclined to think, to faulty night vision, but to much more fundamental causes. The R.A.F. doctors did manful service in improving the aids to night vision that to some extent helped our people to hit their target, but something more than a diet of carrots was required. Bennett felt that a highly specialized team was needed to lead our bomber stream to its objective, and so to mark it that the most recently joined crews could put their bombs somewhere near the target. He had many conflicts with "Bomber" Harris and also with Air Marshal Ralph Cochrane, who supported an alternative

[1] Wing Commander D. C. T. Bennett, D.S.O.

method,[1] but in the end the "Pathfinder Force", the *élite* of the night pilots and navigators, came into being.

On 16th August 1942 a Bomber Command order established this force as part of No. 3 Group R.A.F., but operating directly under the Commander-in-Chief. It consisted at first of four squadrons, three of which were of the three types of four-engined aircraft in use at the time, and the fourth was a Wellington squadron.

Throughout the autumn and winter of 1942 the methods of the Pathfinder Force showed promise, but bad weather was still a great hindrance. By this date, however, the radar navigational aids already mentioned were coming into use. "Gee" and "H" had been established already and had given good service. At the end of November "Oboe Mk. 1" was installed in the Mosquitos of No. 109 Squadron and was first tried in "nuisance" raids on nights of heavy cloud.

So, with the flare methods well tried out and radio aids in service, the Pathfinder Force became firmly established by the end of 1942 and was recognized as an essential feature of the bomber offensive.

Throughout January 1943 weather was bad but "Oboe" made operations possible in conditions where previously no attacks could have been attempted.

During this experimental period the Pathfinder Force worked out its own salvation until in January 1943 Bomber Headquarters committed itself to a definite policy. In a directive issued at that time the accepted functions of the Pathfinder Force were outlined and it was established in No. 8 Group under the command of Air Vice-Marshal Bennett. It consisted of Nos. 7, 35, 83, 109 and 156 Squadrons, and its task was:

(1) The location and illumination of the target and the marking of the aiming points.

(2) The build up of illumination round the aiming points by "fireraisers".

(3) Hence to direct the main bomber force on to the target with the maximum accuracy possible.

[1] This method evolved by Group Captain Cheshire was very effective except in cases where very heavy ground opposition was to be expected. In such cases Bennett's procedure was preferable.

The first task was to be carried out by "searcher" aircraft that dropped strings of flares from six to eight miles long in the supposed neighbourhood of the target. As soon as these flares showed up the target then the "illuminators" were to drop short lines of flares to indicate it more clearly. Finally, other aircraft were to mark the aiming-point or points with coloured flares.

In the directive great stress was laid on navigational training, on accurate timing in the dropping of these flares, and the marking of datum points such as lakes or other distinctive features in the neighbourhood of the objective, so as to assist the aircraft of the main force on their final run over the target.

To differentiate between the functions of the various types of marker flares, different colours were used, commonly white, yellow, green and red. The sequence of these colours were varied to prevent the enemy from using similar flares for deception.

In February 1943 "H_2S", already mentioned, came into use. Throughout the month there was bad weather and a high proportion of raids depended on special equipment for locating targets. The exceptions were attacks on Milan, Spezia, and Lorient, where weather was generally good. So, in spite of much cloud, February was the busiest month so far for the Pathfinder Force. Sky-marking was used where ground-marking was impossible. Some trouble was experienced with "Oboe" but, on the whole, this was a most valuable piece of equipment.

So the story continues with alternating success and failure, but undoubtedly heavy blows were dealt to Germany. By the middle of 1943 P.F. technique had become very effective.

This was one development. The institution of a "master of ceremonies", later called the "Master Bomber", was another. By the middle of 1943 all but the Master Bomber technique were in operation. On the 7th August 1943 the first attack employing this new method was launched on Turin. The War Diary of No. 83 Squadron states that on this date 14 aircraft of the squadron, under the control of Wing Commander J. H. Searby, and composed of "blind markers" employing H_2S, visual markers in their support, and backers-up to keep the

ABOVE, *a V1 launching site as used at first,
after bombing, and* BELOW *a modified site*

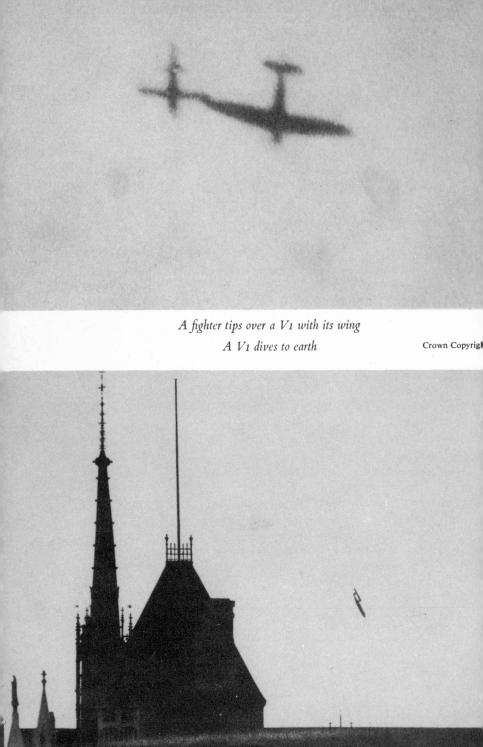

A fighter tips over a V1 with its wing

A V1 dives to earth

supply of flares going, attacked Turin very successfully. The duty of the Master Bomber was to watch the fall of the blind markers on the aiming-point, to correct by his instructions to the visual markers and backers-up the errors made and then announce by R.T. to the bomber stream which of the markers they should use as their aiming-point. This involved the Master Bomber in a prolonged stay in the vicinity of the target, sometimes during the whole of the raid—a most dangerous assignment. In case he became a casualty, two or more captains from the same squadron were briefed as replacements. In the event the scheme worked exceedingly well, and it was decided to adopt it for the raid against the vital target of Peenemünde.

But before the attack took place there was a considerable period of preparation. It was realized that this long and narrow target, lying as a fringe along the coastline, would, in the best of circumstances, be very difficult to hit, even with the new techniques. In an endeavour to ensure success, preliminary practices were carried out on a stretch of British coastline that bore some resemblance to that on which Peenemünde lay. Previous to these exercises, "track in" and "timing" flights were made so as to arrive at the best possible pattern of attack. The great value of these preparations was shown by the results achieved—at first an error of 1,000 yards and, later, only 300 yards, in the mean point of impact of our bombs. In addition, as part of the cover plan, the crews were told that Peenemünde was developing a new form of radar that might become very lethal to our bombers—an *argumentum ad hominem* that bore the authentic touch of "Bomber" Harris! It was considered that this would add point to the exhortations to make the raid a complete success. The crews were also told to attack from not more than 8,000 ft., much below the normal altitude, and that if they did not achieve full success in the first raid it would have to be repeated, regardless of loss, on every suitable night until the target was completely destroyed. In view of this directive there is no question that, in spite of early doubts and hesitations, the Air Staff and Bomber Command went into the battle at full strength, and with the utmost determination.

E

It would seem that Major Sandys' representations and the possibility, never officially admitted, that the rockets might use an atomic warhead, had been completely convincing to the Chiefs of Staff. But the Prime Minister and Lord Cherwell were still sceptical.

On the 17th August, 83 Squadron was again detailed as "marker", with Searby as Master Bomber. On this date it was rumoured in the squadron that he had been promoted to Group Captain, and in this case the rumour "was not a lying jade".

Now follows Searby's own account of the raid.

"Briefing.

At 1500 hours the aircrews assembled in the briefing room and the target for the night was made known to them. Previously, the crew selected for the master bomber rôle had received careful and detailed briefing with the aid of models and the tactics to be used had been worked out thoroughly. A.O.C. No. 8 Group personally supervised this part of the planning, and since there were three aiming points to be taken in turn considerable judgement was needed in regard to the timing. Much interest was displayed by the Squadron since this operation represented a change from the succession of attacks on the Ruhr and similar objectives. Such attacks were invariably made in the face of heavy opposition, and it was with some relief the crews learned that tonight we would be going to a target which was out of the common run; that it would be well defended was expected, but at least we should not have to bore through a forest of waving searchlight beams and concentrated fire from the Ruhr defences. Variety means a great deal in war.

The briefing began and the familiar routine we knew so well. The objective was described and its importance emphasized by the Intelligence Officer, who drew attention to the defences. It seemed there was not much heavy flak, but a quantity of light anti-aircraft guns and plenty of night fighter activity. He dealt thoroughly with the whole area surrounding Peenemünde, and the route we should fly to get there. Then followed the details of the target indicators or marker bombs which each aircraft would carry, and the method of release, whilst Signals and Gunnery Officers in turn briefed the crews on the procedures to be adopted concerning the radio and air to air gunnery tactics. These were followed by the Meteorological Officer, who gave a description of the weather we could expect to find on the route and over the actual target in terms of wind velocity, cloud height, and visibility. This part of the briefing was concluded by the Navigation Officer who dealt in detail with the Flight Plan and the time schedules.

My own part of the briefing came next and I outlined the tactics we should employ on the route and over the target. We would fly low across the North Sea as far as the Eastern coast of Denmark, and in this way endeavour to escape the attention of the German Radar until we were close to the coastline; this would give only the minimum time in which the enemy could alert his night fighters. Jutland would be crossed at a low altitude and once over the Danish Islands aircraft would climb to 7,000 feet for the remainder of the journey to Peenemünde. The tactics to be used when meeting opposition in the form of flak, searchlights, and night fighters were explained and the necessity for making accurate runs over the aiming points emphasized. The various crews were given their special tasks. There were the Blind Markers who, by means of their Radar, would mark the area with yellow flares—the Visual Markers, who, with the assistance of the yellow flares would identify and mark the exact aiming points—the the Backers Up, whose job was to keep the pot boiling by dropping additional markers on the previously marked aiming points throughout the attack. My own task was that of Master Bomber, and in this rôle I would be responsible for directing the bombing force over the full period of the operation by means of the voice radio equipment we carried. If necessary we, as a crew, would drop additional markers to correct the bombing and at the same time give instructions cancelling those which were likely to mislead the main bombing force. Three deputy master bombers had been detailed from other squadrons in the Group, to take over in the event we were unable to perform this work as a result of interference by the enemy. All crews would maintain a listening watch on their voice radios for guidance from the master bomber crew."

The plan that was made for the attack took into account that the Germans were very sensitive to any approach from the South Baltic coast. A number of successful attacks on Berlin had been made from this direction and Hitler "had not been amused".

Each of the aiming-points was to be bombarded for 15 minutes, and so the whole raid was to be over in three-quarters of an hour.

Searby again takes up the story:

"Route to the Target
    It was a fine summer evening and an hour before the scheduled time of take-off all crews were ready and out at their aeroplanes making the final checks of their equipment. At 2150 hours I was airborne with my crew in Lancaster 'William' and set course for the Danish coast. We took off ahead of the Squadron since it was our intention to arrive over the target early, making a low approach from sea-wards. In this way we hoped to obtain a good view of the three aiming points chosen by Intelligence for their impact and which were roughly in line, and generally familiarize ourselves with the landmarks, checking them against the model and photographs which we had studied previously. Every prominent feature which would help us to locate the aiming points had been memorized and we carried in our heads a mental picture of what we expected to find. Additionally, we had memorized certain features on the run in from the sea so that we should be able to make an accurate approach without the necessity for wasting time flying around at a low altitude in an effort to find what we wanted.
    From the Norfolk coast to Denmark the weather was clear. We flew a few hundred feet above the sea and after two hours we made a landfall to the north of the island of Romo. Our low approach over the North Sea resulted in the German early warning Radar receiving little or no warning, whilst the fine weather with a rising full moon dead ahead enabled us to pinpoint our position accurately over the coast. The island of Sylt lay a few miles to the south, and was our chief source of anxiety at this stage, since it contained a night fighter airfield; but all was quiet. At 1,000 feet we crossed the mainland of Denmark

and the navigator worked hard to keep the aeroplane to its time schedule. We wished to avoid those points of land in the Little Belt which were known to contain light flak batteries and it was important, therefore, to maintain a precise track.

Leaving the coast of Jutland we altered course to the east and commenced flying over numerous small islands with their white-washed farm houses and clearly defined shore lines. Weather was excellent. A sharp look out was maintained by the mid-upper and tail gunners, and by the bomb aimer lying in the nose of the aeroplane. The wireless operator stood in the astro dome looking forwards and up into the moonlit sky for enemy night fighters which we could expect to meet from now on. The Germans would be fully alerted by this time and our track across Denmark plotted. However, an aircraft flying low over the sea is not easy to discern even in bright moonlight, and we were far too low for the big radars situated on the mainland to pick us up.

Over Longland we were engaged by light flak which was not effective, and after a short time we began to look ahead for the large island of Rugen; this would prove a useful landmark from which to make our later approach to the target. We skirted Rugen to the north to avoid flak, and having pinpointed our position commenced the final run toward the small peninsula on which the German experimental establishment is situated. So far everything had gone well. As we neared the land we noted a thin sheet of layer type cloud, but it was above us and would not hinder us in our task. A few seconds more and we had crossed the coastline with our objective in front of us.

It was apparent that the Germans were alerted since the smoke canisters surrounding the area were just starting up and smoke was commencing to drift across the airfield, spreading to the hangars and buildings, but it was far too late to be effective. Light anti-aircraft fire was directed against us, but it proved inaccurate, and we flew around the area taking careful note of those landmarks adjacent to the three aiming points. We then turned out to sea and climbed to 5,000 feet, taking up a position just off the land, with our voice radio switched on. We were now ready for the operation to commence.

The Attack

Shortly before 'H' hour the first group of yellow markers went down in the settlement area where the scientists and technicians were housed, and only a matter of a few seconds later a bright red target indicator was seen to fall amongst them; this was the aiming point marker and we flew directly over it from the direction of the oncoming bombers to assess its accuracy. It was well placed and, as near as we were able to judge, right on the pin. Exactly at 0200 hours the main force commenced a heavy bombardment, and we observed the fall of the high explosive and incendiary bombs in good concentration—fires were starting and beginning to spread. By this time the defences were more active and a moderate number of heavy batteries were seen to open up. After a few minutes another run was made across the target and it was noted that some of the later target indicators had overshot the aiming point, whereupon an immediate broadcast was sent out to the oncoming bombers informing them of the situation. This had the effect of pulling the bombing back, and later marking by the Pathfinders was of high quality. We kept up a continuous running commentary to all Pathfinder and main force crews informing them as to the accuracy of the marking and exhorting them to maintain the high standard."

The Master Bomber, continuing his runs over the target so low to observe results that he was in grave danger of being bombed by his own friends, then ordered the attack to commence, using greens as the aiming-points. Some further reds fell into the sea, and the backers-up were ordered to ignore them.

Searby kept on circling the target in the opposite direction to the main stream so as to join the later comers, and every time he went out to sea he was particularly annoyed by flak ships that fired very accurately at him. He found this attention after some minutes "monotonous". Backing-up continued and some greens also fell into the sea, resulting in a further warning to the main force, of which the leading squadrons were approaching. Searby instructed these aircraft to ignore "all but the right-hand greens, which were considered to be on the target". By 0210 the attack was going well, but the enemy smoke-screen was becoming effective, flak was heavy, and enemy fighters, who had been diverted southwards towards Berlin by a feint attack made by a few Mosquitos, were beginning to arrive in large numbers. At this time at least two of our bombers were seen to go down in flames. Many single-engined aircraft were seen silhouetted against the burning target. The full moon and the well-lit background coupled with the fact that our aircraft were attacking at around 8,000 ft. presented the enemy with really first-class conditions for making their kills.

Searby had thus led the attack to the point where the target was well marked, and it was for the main force to so place its bombs on the markers that the Peenemünde research station and its scientist staff would be wiped out. By 0215 the marking of the second aiming-point had started. Sample reports from this main force are taken from the operations book of No. 156 Squadron—equipped with Lancasters.

Pilot-Officer Soper, captain of aircraft J.A. 502, records: "Target indicators dropped by special equipment (H₂S) at 0209 hours, height 13,000 ft. At 0215 attacked, bombing centre of yellow target indicators." Flying-Officer Lutz, captain of E.D. 296, states, "After second yellows a good concentration was achieved." Both pilots complained of scattered red indicators. Flight-Lieutenant Vincent—J.A. 698—attacked at 0238 hours from 12,000 ft. on "well-concentrated green markers". The Master Bomber's instructions during the previous fifteen minutes had achieved this result.

Earlier, other pilots of 156 Squadron had formed the opinion that by 0025 hours the fires were taking a good hold and that "an excellent prang had been achieved". Flak was described as slight, but by 0241 night-fighters were very active in the bright moonlight.

Squadron-Leader Huntley-Wood—E.D. 832, No. 207 Squadron—attacked at 0051. He identified the target but did not observe the result of his own bombs "owing to the intensity of the bombing. The Pathfinder (coloured marker) technique was excellent and the Master Bomber's instructions of very great help. The target had the appearance of being well and truly hit".

Squadron-Leader Bayne, however, flying W. 5006, heard nothing from the Master Bomber, but Flying-Officer Kirkwood in W. 4185 heard him very clearly and considered his instructions very helpful. Normal service does not seem to have been working in W. 5006.

Pilot-Officer Fitzgerald in W. 4120 attacked at 0254 hours. What he saw at that time made him very optimistic. "A return visit to Peenemünde by Bomber Command will be unnecessary."

Captains of aircraft from No. 44 (Rhodesia) Squadron confirmed that the Master Bomber's instructions were of the greatest help. No. 44 attacked at about 0242 and four minutes later observed the target almost blotted out by flames and smoke. From No. 7 Squadron came the statement: "It should be a good raid. The most concentrated effort yet seen." No. 35 Squadron which attacked earlier at 0225 confirmed the value of the Master Bomber technique. "A terrific concentration of target indicators." Interspersed amongst these statements are reports of very big explosions (other than bombs) that occurred from time to time. These must have been the fuel and warhead stores going up in flames and smoke, the fuel and explosives intended to aid the destruction of Britain.

As the attack developed on the second aiming-point—the workshops, drawing-offices and testing plant—more of the green markers overshot, and a further warning was issued by Searby to the backers-up. The main force was ordered to ignore the southerly greens (Searby had realized the possibility of confusion arising from the use of "left" and "right" —an earlier fault of his) and bomb those lying to the north. A further run over the target—officially his seventh, though privately he admits to fourteen—showed him that the second aiming-point was well covered, though some reds were still falling into the sea, probably on account of the smoke from the screens and from the huge fires that were now blazing fiercely. By this time many more fighters had arrived and Searby observed a number of our bombers being shot down.

At 0242 hours, 50 minutes after his first run over the objective, Searby again warned the backers-up that they were dropping greens into the sea. A further run over the target did, however, show him that both aiming-points were well covered. Though burning woods hampered his observations, he was satisfied that the attack was going well. At 0230 hours the marking of the third aiming-point commenced. This was difficult owing to the smoke from fires and exploding bombs. Here some assistance was lent by Searby's bomb-aimer who, because he had a complete picture in his mind's eye from the beginning of the attack, was able to guide and direct the marking aeroplanes. Confirmation was given by the two deputy Master Bombers that the third aiming-point was now being covered. Even so, this did not last long, for the chaotic conditions below rendered accurate assessment out of the question, and the spectacle afforded by the whole target area was one of utter confusion—tremendous fires were sweeping the targets and the smoke billowed up to a great height.

Aircraft of No. 427 Royal Canadian Air Force (Halifaxes) commenced their run over the objective at about 0230. Flight-Sergeant Champion in Dk 253 bombed the green indicators from 10,000 ft., greatly helped by Searby's running commentary. In his opinion the raid was "a good effort". Flying-Officer Baum bombed from 9,000 ft. and considered that the Master Bomber procedure was not only most helpful but a morale-booster. Sergeant Schmidt in Dk 227 had a successful fight with a Me 109, which his crew shot down—not before some considerable damage had been done to his aircraft.

All the crews of this squadron reported that they thought highly of the work of the Master Bomber. No. 97 Straits Settlements Squadron also bombed successfully, though detailed observations were difficult due to smoke. Two large explosions were seen at 0238 and 0248.

By this time a very large fire was visible in the target area, though its exact significance was not clear owing to the amount of woodland that was also burning and the volume of smoke from the smoke-screens.

The whole attack was over in less than an hour. In his final run, one of many over the target, Wing Commander Searby was unable to distinguish individual buildings owing to the tremendous fires sweeping the area. While trying to

follow the main force homewards he was attacked by an old
Me 110 painted grey. The first attack was avoided, but at the
second his rear-gunner got in a good burst and the enemy
probably crashed in the target area. During his prolonged stay
over Peenemünde the Master Bomber observed enemy night-
fighters showing great activity and many of our aircraft going
down in flames. On the homeward journey near Langeland
there was further trouble from these fighters which, in the
conditions of excellent visibility due to clear weather and full
moonlight, were able to operate with a minimum of ground
control and a maximum of effect.

Forty of our bombers did not return from this raid, and
from those reaching base in safety reports of 51 attacks and
claims of five enemy destroyed were received. Many night
photographs were taken and the general impression held by
all the crews was that the attack though costly had been highly
successful.

The Master Bomber's feelings, as he flew back and forth
across the target, must have been very mixed. At first delighted at the skilful planting of the marker flares on the
target and the smooth progression of the attack. Then he must
have experienced moments of anxiety when the markers became more scattered as pilots, either less skilful or more con-
fused by the enemy's counter-measures, dropped their load far
from the aiming-point. Added to this preoccupation would be
his periodical concern for his aircraft and crew as he flew over
the flak-ships that had, to some extent, got his measure. This
nerve-shaking experience must have occurred certainly a dozen
times. It requires a type of cool courage of a very high order
to keep on flying into a danger area for an hour on end and
at the same time evaluate with precision the progress of an
aid raid of such magnitude. The cold breath of death must
have often been in his nostrils. Later in the raid he was to see
British aircraft bearing, if not his own friends, at least his
fellow countrymen, whirling to earth like flaming torches,
while the earth, sea and sky shook to the thud of bursting
bombs and the assault of the German anti-aircraft guns. On
this night of flame and silver, of fire, smoke and shining moonlight, he must have passed through periods of exaltation, of

vast depression, and finally of a certain grim satisfaction that Peenemünde, at heavy cost, had been well and truly "pranged".

Now for Major-General Dornberger, asleep in his bunk after calling defence H.Q., who told him that enemy bombers were massing north of the island of Rugen, "direction of attack unknown". Into his slumbers penetrated certain noises. Half awake, he believed that these were due to the experimental firing with an anti-dive-bomber and anti-tank weapon that he had authorized that evening. He started almost automatically to count the explosions. Not until these had exceeded the test he had agreed upon did he realize that these were enemy bombs exploding on Peenemünde—the marker bombs that were the prelude to the main attack. He had hardly dressed before the doors of his house were blown in, windows smashed and roof-tiles scattered. On his doorstep he saw what he has described with vigour and a certain poetic sense. "I stood transfixed. The scene that met my gaze had a sinister and appalling beauty of its own. I was confronted as though through a curtain of rosy gauze by an almost incredible stage-setting in subdued lighting and colours." Those of us who were in London during the blitz of autumn 1940 will recognize the authentic touch. The people of Coventry will remember the moon shining through the "fragile cottony clouds" that were produced by enormous fires in their city. So, and not otherwise, did Dornberger see what he thought was his whole enterprise, his whole life, going up in flames and smoke. His chief warden reported to him that the Measurement Shop was on fire, the assembly workshop blazing, and the component and repair workshops starting to burn. Worse was to follow. The fires grew and the rosy haze turned to scarlet and black, with vast flames and smoke-clouds reaching to heaven. Dornberger sent detachments of his devoted team to strive to save the vitals of Peenemünde—the drawing-offices, with their safes and filing-cabinets and the telephone exchange badly damaged by a heavy bomb. His interest in keeping the place warm in the following winter—it was warm enough at the moment and his detachment must be admired—made him concentrate on saving the boiler house! He speaks also with pride of his successful effort at saving the Measurement House which contained the Instruments Guidance and Measurement Departments, at the time the most valuable part of the work. Elsewhere the fires had taken too strong a hold and the reinforcements of fire-fighters and labour that were arranged for under the emergency plan had not arrived. In Dornberger's own words, "Due to the weight of the attack, our carefully laid scheme covering all eventualities and several times rehearsed, had failed completely." But at least one copy of all production schemes, drawings and files had been lodged elsewhere.

Personnel losses were high, but Dornberger only admits to the death of two key men, Dr. Thiel and Chief Engineer Walther. The slave-workers in the settlement—over 500 of them died—and other dwellers there were the principal sufferers.

The evidence appears conclusive, and is borne out by the results of many other apparently most successful raids by Bomber Command. The effect of the attack on Peenemünde, with its heavy loss in aircraft and valuable aircrew, unquestionably delayed the launching of the attack on Britain by V2. According to Goebbels for not more than a few weeks—eight at the most. Dornberger suggests four weeks. The resilience of the German war machine and of the German people is surely one of the outstanding facts of the Hitler war. It might almost be called miraculous, but even so these statements cannot be believed. Six months is the more likely figure, and this was the view of the Chief of the Air Staff, Air Chief Marshal Portal, as expressed at the end of August 1943.

General Eisenhower, writing of his "Crusade in Europe", states that the development and employment of the V weapons was greatly delayed by the bombing of Peenemünde, and other places where they were manufactured. He goes on to say: "It seems likely that, if the Germans had succeeded in perfecting and using these weapons six months earlier than they did, our invasion of Europe would have proved exceedingly difficult, perhaps impossible. I feel sure that if they had succeeded in using these weapons over a six-months' period, and particularly if they had made the Portsmouth-Southampton area one of their principal targets, "Overlord" might have been written off.

Not everyone would agree with this summing-up, but that the war might well have been greatly prolonged is fairly certain.

Hitler's vacillations and the changes in priority of the rocket programme imposed very serious delays on both V1 and V2. But these six months were vital. They carried the date for launching the attack across the border line where the invasion of Europe was timed to take place.

Photographs taken after the attack show that the airfield and the Luftwaffe camp were untouched. They were not in the plan, which concentrated on the home of V2. Thus it is clear that the V1 programme was not seriously affected by the bombardment of Peenemünde. But other causes conspired to hold it back. V2 was delayed directly by the attack and about this there is no question.

On the whole it seems that the setbacks of all sorts to the V1 programme were the most significant. Heavy bombardment by V1 of the invasion assembly areas might have partially, if not completely, disrupted the Allied plans. The concentration of vulnerable targets on the south coast of England offered a hostage to fortune of immense potential value to the enemy, and his inability to destroy or even damage these targets seriously before the Allied Armada set off for the coast of Normandy was one of the most decisive factors in the destruction of Hitler's Reich. So our losses over Peenemünde, grievous as they were, did nothing to detract from the value of the War Cabinet's decision "to launch the heaviest possible night attack . . . on the first occasion when conditions were suitable". At the time, however, the British were not to know that the bombing of Peenemünde was the first phase of the successful invasion of Europe, leading to the defeat of Hitler's Germany. Now it must be classed as one of the decisive operations of the war.

There is a sequel to the story of the Peenemünde raid and its effect on the production of V2. Hitler was so concerned at the consequence of this disaster that he ordered a removal of the "Revenge" organization to Blizna in Poland. This move, added to the dispersal of the surviving scientists and their equipment which took place immediately after the raid, must have produced a very great disorganization in the plans for launching the V-weapon attack on Britain. We can discount Dornberger's estimate of four and Goebbels' suggestion of eight weeks' delay as merely wishful thinking. Those of us who had knowledge of the dislocation of our radar programme resulting from the move in 1939 of the Telecommunications Research Establishment from Bawdsey to the North of Scotland, and then back to Dorset in 1940, can have a very shrewd idea as to the extent to which plans were upset, schedules of production scrapped and results retarded.

In *Destiny Can Wait* the Poles recount how it was only towards the end of 1943 that information was received about mysterious preparations—not action—which were under way at Blizna S.S. Military Exercise Camp in South Poland. The observers of the Underground reported that "closely guarded railway consignments began to arrive, the loads being covered with tarpaulins and conveyed on enormous railway wagons of a special type. Concrete emplacements were being constructed in the camp and numerous commissions came and went. . . ." Finally, in January 1944, nearly six months after the Peenemünde raid—a significant date—the mysterious weapon was fired for the first time. A few days later a report was received by the Polish Home Army Intelligence that the weapon had struck and destroyed several cottages at a distance of nearly 200 miles from Blizna. (What did it matter to the Germans that Poles and Polish property were destroyed by the experiment! Base peasants of an inferior race, that was their proper fate.) The report gave a few bare facts and added that within a very short time a German party arrived on the scene of the explosion and gathered up every fragment of the missile that could be found. More of the projectiles were fired. Some exploded in the air and though the line of fire remained more or less constant the "scatter" of the points of impact covered a distance of 50 or 60 miles and in rare cases even more. Motorized German units patrolled the line of fire and the nearest to the point of impact would dash in to collect every scrap of the weapon left by the explosion. The Polish patrols also operated along the line of flight, but under grave handi-

cap. They lacked the fast motor-cars needed, and every move
had to be executed with more than one eye on the nearest
German formation. The Gestapo was active and, if caught, or
if even suspicion fell upon them, the Poles could only expect
torture and death. The German collecting-parties could take
their time and make a thorough search. For the Poles it was
"quick in and quick out", but in spite of the advantages
possessed by the enemy the Poles laid their hands on a certain
amount of material. Much of it was valueless, but from time
to time essential parts such as turbo-compressors, fuel reser-
voirs, rudder chains and electrical equipment were captured.
Later the "scatter" became less, not more than 10 miles. This
was very helpful to the Germans and equally unhelpful to the
Poles, who might quite reasonably have, at this point, given
up the unequal struggle. But their patience, skill and courage
had its reward. One of the rockets dropped on the bank of the
River Bug and did not explode. This was near the village of
Sarmaki where some of the "Underground" were active.
These men reached the spot in time to roll the weapon into
the water and by various common-sense devices, such as water-
ing large numbers of cattle upstream of the V2, made the
water so muddy that the German search-parties failed in their
intention. That night the Poles fished the weapon out of the
water and in great stealth dismantled it and removed the vital
parts. Much courage was needed for this operation. Not only
were the Germans close by, but the business of making the
charge safe by the light of shrouded torches and in complete
silence demanded an ice-cold nerve as well as great skill.

The results of this capture were communicated to London
from whence came the prompt demand that the vital components should be sent there for examination. Then followed an
operation which, for dramatic value, was quite remarkable.
We British are always considered to be masters of the art of
meiosis, but the comment on the operation in *Destiny Can Wait*
is certainly in a class by itself. "A British Dakota picked up a
number of Polish Underground V.I.P.s by arrangement on
the night of 25th July 1944 in Southern Poland and brought
them to Brindisi in Italy. They then flew on to Great Britain
and among them was probably no one more eagerly awaited

than a Polish engineer whose luggage consisted solely of technical documents and more than 100 lb. weight of flying-bomb parts." (In fact V2 and not V1 parts.) What actually happened is recounted in Bernard Newman's book *They Saved London*. By arrangement with the Royal Air Force a disused German airstrip with the code name of "Motyl" was designated as the picking-up point. It had been used once before by the R.A.F. where in a matter of six minutes the operation of landing, unloading, reloading and taking off had been carried out successfully. The Polish party arrived with their precious burden of V2 parts during the afternoon before the "pick-up" and 400 members of the Underground picketed the woods surrounding the strip, which was found to be somewhat boggy due to recent heavy rain. To their horror a succession of German fighters arrived and carried out a series of landings and take-offs, but soon it was obvious that these were only training flights and before dark the last had left. At the appointed time the Dakota touched down—a fine feat of navigation. Quickly it was unloaded and the party of V.I.P.s embarked, together with the V2 equipment. The engines were opened up—and the aircraft refused to budge. At first it was considered to have bogged down, but frantic digging and pushing failed to help. The pilot then concluded that his brakes must have jammed. There was only one thing to do. The oil pipes leading to the brakes were cut, and after more digging, pushing and violent slewing of the aircraft, it finally released itself and in a practically "stalled" attitude wallowed off the ground. It had taken an hour to escape and already the German patrols were approaching. The cutting of the oil pipes had put all the other hydraulics out of action and the undercarriage could not be retracted until water from the emergency ration was poured into the oil reservoir, thus giving enough pressure to enable the wheels to be raised.

So, via Brindisi, the secrets of V2 reached London. The pilot's report of this fantastic episode concludes with the remark, "Apart from some slight excitement at the airstrip everything went very smoothly." A Polish officer who was present says: "This report is a magnificent piece of under-statement. Only the minimum of imagination is necessary to picture the intense drama of the scene. At first, everything goes according to plan—no hitches—all the V.I.P.s present and the precious equipment safely packed in the aircraft. Then the engines of the Dakota are started. As they have functioned faultlessly on the flight into Poland there is no need to test them. Cockpit routine is carried out, crew check made and then the pilot releases the brakes and opens the throttles. Nothing happens—the aircraft remains stationary, throbbing and vibrating to the surge of the engines. The pilot wears a puzzled frown and the second pilot hastily repeats his cockpit drill to see that he has forgotten nothing. After some seconds the pilot shuts the engines off. Anxious enquiry comes from the onlookers—the second pilot gets out of the aircraft and looks at the wheels. They do not seem sufficiently sunk in the wet ground to be unable to move. However, shovels are soon brought from a neighbouring cottage, but digging does not help. In the end the pilot decides that the brakes are to blame. The hydraulic leads are cut, and with the Germans not half a mile away the aircraft lumbers off the ground to safety. We of the Underground melt into the darkness of the woods."

But some weeks before this success—on June 12th 1944— the first V1 was launched against Britain. Thus the gallant work carried out by the Polish Underground movement had done little more than to confirm all the previous information received from them and from other sources, information which was to receive very practical reinforcement from the explosion of revenge weapons in the London area. But we now knew how the V2 worked and to some extent our problem was simplified. It was not radio-guided—and its warhead weighed only 1,000 lb. or so. V1 at the moment appeared the more dangerous weapon as it presented a difficult problem to our fighters and to our A.A. defences, a problem which was only solved after some months of trial and experiment.

CHAPTER VI

THE STORY OF V1—*continued*

REFERENCE has already been made to the early history of V1—the flying bomb—in its days as a private venture of German scientists and industrialists. Since it was in some sense a flying machine, the German Air Force took it under its wing in the middle 1930s and, as has been said, Engineer Bree, at the Reichsluftfart Ministerium, was put in charge of development. When Peenemünde was opened as a research and experimental station the G.A.F. project moved in with the Army's V2 establishment. Thus the two organizations grew side by side on the Peenemünde peninsula, a mile or so apart, with their respective camps separated by an area of very dense woodland. The G.A.F. camp was called Zempin and was in charge of Major Stahms. Engineer Temme was made responsible for the mechanical side of the work, but much of the development and all the manufacture was in the hands of civilian firms, of which Fieseler was the most important.

By early 1943 progress had been made which justified the decision of the Long Range Bombardment commission to which reference has already been made. In April a certain Colonel Max Wachtel was sent for by General von Axthelm, and behind locked doors, and after a suitable toast in good French brandy, was told that he was to be in charge of V operations. He was ordered to report to Peenemünde and be ready to start operations in France by December.

Max Wachtel, an officer in the German Artillery during the First World War, retired from the armed forces in 1918 and subsequently worked with industrial firms. In 1936 he placed himself at the disposal of the new Wehrmacht. He was restored to the active list again with the rank of Captain, and from then on belonged to the anti-aircraft artillery. His gifts as a leader of men were soon recognized by the higher command, so that in peace-time as well as at the beginning of the war he was always entrusted with special tasks. Thus he was put in charge of the development and operation of the so-called "Siebel ferries", which were shallow draft barges equipped with heavy anti-aircraft artillery used for operations in the Channel. These barges were also used to interfere with Russian supplies for Leningrad on Lake Ladoga. Subsequently, until his appointment to the VI group by General von Axthelm, he was in command of the training regiment of the Anti-aircraft Artillery School at Rerick, holding the rank of Lieutenant-Colonel. His appointment as military leader of the development and operation of VI constituted a very special recognition of his organizational talents and his flexibility (which may be explained by his many years of work with industry) in successfully dealing with the unusual.

Peenemünde was to some extent a rest cure, but the technical problems involved in the launching of VI were many and tiresome. Wachtel's unit, entitled the Leehr und Erprobungskommando Wachtel, battled against these difficulties with some success, and in strong competition with Dornberger's V2 outfit. There must have been considerable jealousy on both sides. In his book *V2* Dornberger states that in the experiments before the Long Range Bombardment Commission V2 functioned faultlessly while VI had 100% failures. Wachtel denies this furiously and claims that he had equal success. This is probably true, since the Commission decided to proceed with the development of both weapons.

On the night of 17th/18th August the G.A.F. station at Zempin was at peace. Nothing disturbed the slumbers of its personnel except for the drone of an unusual number of aircraft overhead. Only the air-raid warning staff were awake, together with the crews manning the anti-aircraft guns. Presently there were "noises off" and the lighter sleepers stirred uneasily and turned over in their bunks. Fräulein Hanna Reitsch, the well-known woman pilot who later was to fly the experimental manned VI suicide weapon, was so deeply asleep that she heard nothing.

Colonel Wachtel states that next morning his camp woke to its normal life. Not one bomb had dropped on it and the window-cleaners were polishing the shining panes of the officers' mess. To his intense astonishment he discovered that the V2 sites had been largely destroyed by British air attack during the previous night. His only explanation of V1's escape and the unbroken slumbers of his people is that the west wind blew the smoke of the screens away from his camp, thus persuading the bombers (if persuasion was needed!) that the main target lay under the smoke. He claims that the dense woodland between the two camps so deadened the noise of the bombing that it was almost unnoticeable. This is a strange, an almost incredible, story, but the fact remains that the home of V1 was hardly touched. This may well be the explanation of German statements that the production of V1 was not in any way delayed by the attack on Peenemünde.

Wachtel's main concern was the erratic behaviour of the weapon. Time and again when launched from the ramp it would topple over and dive into the ground a few hundred yards from the site. A number of launchings were filmed and it was discovered that the blast from the motor was striking the elevators and deflecting them so sharply that a nose-dive was inevitable. The addition of a baffle plate partly cured this defect, but it continued to plague launching operations until the end of the campaign. In addition, the gyro controls were not fully effective and on occasion the weapon, having reached a height of some hundreds of feet on its proper course, would do a sharp about-turn and fall amongst its friends.

In spite of this trouble, and Wachtel's protestations that development had not reached the point where production could start, he received orders that the bombardment of London should start in the late autumn of 1943. Wachtel's attitude seems reasonable. The first time V1 took the air was when it was launched, unpowered and gliding only, from a Kondor aircraft in December 1942, under the guidance of Herr Fieseler. The first powered launch from a ramp was carried out on Christmas Eve of that year. To go into mass production six months afterwards, and to expect to use the weapon operationally in less than a year, will strike all technical people as an act of lunacy.

However, orders are orders, and the Flak Regiment 155W began to be formed from the Erprobungs und Sonder Kommando, the first battery taking shape in May 1943. The regiment was complete by 1st November. It was composed of four Abteilungen, and each Abteilungen had four batteries and 16 launching platforms. Abteilung No. 1 went to France in December, to be followed in succession by the remaining three.

The higher organization of the Regiment was as follows. A new Corps, No. 65, was formed to control all Revenge Weapon Operations as from 15th December 1943. For man-power the Regiment depended on Luftflotte 2; for basic organization on Luftgau Belgium, Northern France, and for training on the General der Flakwaffe. This organization was modified from time to time, but in general the 65th Corps remained in control, much to Colonel Wachtel's discontent, for the Corps was commanded by one General-Leutnant Heinemann, aged sixty-seven, and so appointed because he was a great ballistic expert. Wachtel's staff refer to him as "a good old man", but he appears to have been a mere figurehead. The real leader in 65th Corps was Walter, the Colonel on the General Staff, whose decisions soon betrayed that he was completely ignorant of the operational needs of V1, and so was constantly at odds with the experts of the Regiment.

While these preparations were being made the area of operations in France was surveyed and work commenced on the launching sites. This was at the end of August 1943, and in September Colonel Wachtel visited Luftflotte 3 staff in Paris for discussions on the future of the project. Target maps had already been made and were handed to Wachtel, and the War Diary of the Regiment indicates that great hopes were held that the bombardment could, as already ordered, start in December. By mid-September the special meteorological service required for operations was set up covering the area Dinan, Le Mans, Laon–Athies, Grosselies, Abbeville–Caen.

By 23rd September 40,000 workers were engaged on building the launching sites. Some of these men had toiled to make the large sites at Watten, intended to be used as a storage centre. This had been largely destroyed by the VIIIth United States Air Force and, in fact, was never used. Building opera-tions had not proceeded smoothly. Though the sites them-selves, apart from Watten, had not been attacked, the Allied air operations against communications had greatly delayed the provision of the necessary material. In addition, the labour force, already believing in Germany's ultimate defeat, bolted at the sound of aircraft overhead. The promises made to Wachtel failed to be fulfilled and, in addition, shortages of manpower and material for the necessary extensions to the training programme at Zempin began to affect the programme. Manpower for the batteries also fell well below the promises made by Goering. Of 680 men due to reach the Regiment by mid-August only a trickle had arrived. Of 400 men that should have been sent to the factories making V1, so as to gain experience in its handling, only 220 were under training. Thus the first Abteilung had to be despatched to France after having fired a token number of bombs at Zempin —poor preparation for what was before them. Hopes of starting the bombardment in December began to fade.

One other matter was to frustrate and irritate Wachtel. For some months there had been on his staff a Dr. Sommerfeld, renowned in the G.A.F. as a teacher of ballistics and who had been successfully engaged at Peenemünde in working out a method of plotting the fall of the V weapons. Considerable progress had been made in this art and it was particularly annoying that 65th Corps, in May 1943, should insist that another method devised by a Hauptsturm-Führer Richter should be tried out as an alternative. The new system soon failed but considerable friction was caused between the Corps and the Regiment. Wachtel's protests against the waste of time involved earned him a severe reprimand.

A much greater anxiety that affected Wachtel's mind lay in the failure of German industry to provide an adequate supply of V1. Many of the weapons delivered to the Regiment were either unmodified to actual standards or were short of essential parts. The suggestion made in September that the Volkswagon works at Fallerleben, alone undertaking series production, would deliver 5,000 a month was manifestly wishful thinking. By 5th November only four per day were being delivered and this was barely enough for test and training purposes at Zempin. Even then at least 200 man hours of work per bomb were required to make them serviceable. This

amount of effort might have been justifiable on the bombs
used for experimental purposes, but if it was to be necessary
on each of the "operational" bombs the outlook was indeed
bleak. In the result, the bombs of the first series were produced
and put aside as useless.

The Regiment received a further setback when representatives of Hitler's Headquarters informed the staff on the
12th November that the promised production of 5,000 per
month could not be expected before June 1944. Meanwhile,
the desired minimum of 1,500 monthly was purely theoretical
and would not be achieved until well after the deadline of
December 1943. Colonel Wachtel is not a talkative man, but
when he speaks the quality of his speech is explosive. His
Chief Staff Officer, Hauptman Grothues, Major Schwennesen,
and his A.D.C., Major Dahms, must often, at this time, have
been the recipients of what is vulgarly known as an "ear-full".

More was to follow. In December, control of Regiment
155W was transferred entirely from Luftflotte 3 to 65th Corps.
That was bad enough—it gave Oberst Walter more opportunity for bedevilling Wachtel. But on 20th December began
the Allied air attacks on the launching sites. These attacks
were carried out on a scale and with a persistence that made
it quite clear that the locations of the Regiment's sites had
been accurately plotted and that the Allies had realized the
threat that lay in the VI bombardment of the United Kingdom.

According to the Regimental War Diary, relations between
it and the 65th Corps had always been strained, and for this
there is ample evidence. Each apparently resented the other's
existence. The old-fashioned ballistic expert, General-Leutnant Heinemann, egged on by the ambitious Walter, was
always at odds in any arguments with the forceful and forward-
looking Wachtel. In these arguments 65th Corps lost no
opportunity of making it clear to the Regiment that it held
the ultimate authority, and that its views must prevail. Walter
and Wachtel were at daggers drawn, and being of the same
rank it was clear that they could afford to be very rude to each
other—with impunity. Not till the war was almost over was
the energetic Wachtel able to get rid of his enemy through his
influence with S.S. Obergruppenführer Kammler who, as a

general in charge of weapons of this peculiar sort, had an over-riding authority in their use. Wachtel also used his influence with his old friend and ultimate superior General der Flak-waffe von Axthelm, to circumvent the authority of 65th Corps. He never hesitated to point out the lavish staffing and equipment of the Corps, which in fact commanded one regiment and a small organization concerned with the launching of V2. He also was very ready to criticize 65th Corps' lack of technical knowledge and its faulty appreciation of the use of the new weapons.

From the beginning the Corps had visualized the use of V1 in conjunction with the Luftwaffe's bombing attacks.[1] The bomb was to support Germany's diminishing air power and so restore the balance in the air battle. Wachtel is reported to have opposed this view on the grounds that owing to V1's lack of accuracy and its method of delivery he would only have used it as a terror weapon—a form of retaliation for the massive Allied air bombardment of German cities.

This is a most interesting point. Colonel Wachtel, in a recent conversation, most emphatically denied that this was his view. He considered V1 as a means of attacking military targets—in particular the assembly areas of the Allied invasion forces along the south coast of England. However the argument may have developed, the fact remains that von Axthelm told Wachtel that the arrangements made by the 65th Corps had been approved by the Army General Staff and by General Pelz of the 9th Flieger Corps.

It is difficult to draw any real distinction between the views of 65th Corps and those of Wachtel. From the Battle of Britain onwards the operations of the Luftwaffe against the United Kingdom were, in fact, terror attacks against the morale of the population. The veneer of "military objective" wore thin after the bombing of the airfields of the R.A.F. and the air battles over Kent had produced no decisive result. The night bombardment of our cities in the winter of 1940/41 was an indiscriminate attack on the civilians inhabiting them.

---

[1] *Note.*—Colonel Wachtel claims that this was not the case, but the War Diary of the Regiment gives a different impression, possibly erroneous.

65th Corps' conception of the use of V1 was merely an extension of this activity, however it was camouflaged by a fog of words. Hitler's intention was clear. He wanted the V weapons to bring death and destruction to everyone in the United Kingdom—not merely to blot out military camps and establishments. All this leads one to suppose that while Wachtel may at first have been led, by conversations with Hitler, to regard V1 as purely a terror weapon, his hostility to 65th Corps and his natural instinct as a regular soldier may have turned him towards the true objective—the invasion ports. What he wanted was freedom of action, the right to use his weapons with such flexibility as they possessed, and not to be committed to a course of action dictated by the "kind old gentleman" Heinemann, and the adversary Walter. He was not to achieve this object, though he claims that, without authority, fire was directed on one or two occasions on Southampton and Portsmouth.

By the middle of December 1943 some hundred launching sites were in an advanced state of construction on an arc from the Pas de Calais to the Cherbourg Peninsula. The four Abteilungen of 155W were almost ready to start operations on a very modest scale, owing to lack of supplies, when the blow fell. On the 20th December the Allied Air Forces launched a massive assault on the ramps, ski constructions and preparation huts. By April 1944 almost all the sites were either severely damaged or completely destroyed, while the slave-labour employed on them were running at the first sound of an aircraft engine. Casualties to the Regiment were, however, quite light.

Nevertheless, the Regiment's War Diary admits that if damage continued at the rate achieved by the Allies the original system would have to be abandoned. In any case, the projected bombardment timed for late December was quite out of the question. Wachtel was undismayed. A new form of site, easily transportable, hard to detect and quickly assembled, was devised. As a further protection for the new equipment a certain amount of repair work was continued on the old sites in the hope that the enemy would persist with his attacks upon them. It is possible that the percentage system of damage established by the Allies, and which is mentioned in the next chapter, may have prevented much waste of air effort.

The Regimental Diary, rather a doleful recital at this time, estimates that between 15th December 1943 and 31st March 1944 27,000 tons of bombs were dropped on the sites by close on 10,000 aircraft. These figures should be compared with those given from the Allied account in the next chapter.

As a further precaution the most vigorous security measures were put into force in the neighbourhood of the operational areas, and along the lines of communication. One unfortunate lieutenant who left some non-secret papers connected with the Regiment locked up in his billet when he went on leave was court-martialled and sentenced to death.

So far as Colonel Wachtel was personally concerned, in his endeavours to conceal his identity and cover up his movements between Luftflotte 3 Headquarters in Paris and his regimental post, he was accustomed to change his uniform and that of his accompanying staff in Paris taxis on each visit, and he frequently wore a false beard.

These frequent changes of kit and movements of his own headquarters had little effect upon the Allied Intelligence system, but it certainly prevented his laundry from catching up with him! Often he was without clean underclothes for three weeks at a time! The fact that he also changed his name to Wolf may have helped towards this minor disaster. It may well also have prevented him being captured by Allied Security troops after the war. *A quelque chose malheur est bon.*

A very practical security measure that was also adopted was to comb out the unreliable foreign workers employed on the launching sites, amongst whom were a certain number of German-speaking aliens, usually known as Volksdeutsche, and these were replaced by recruits of German origin.

In early spring of 1944 the whole of Flak Regiment 155W was assembled in France and was renamed Flakgruppe Creil. It had not occupied the firing sites for security reasons and the move forward was not to take place until operations were due to commence. Work on the sites themselves continued.

There was continual traffic between France and the training base at Zempin as batteries continued their training, and the

War Diary complains bitterly of this drain on the Regiment's manpower. To add to its difficulties, 65th Corps suddenly withdrew the personnel of Flieger Regiment No. 93, who had hitherto been guarding the sites, and called upon 155W to undertake this duty. In addition, the men of the batteries were to man the Flak weapons that had been provided to protect the sites and to train as well for an anti-invasion rôle. Finally, any work that remained to be done on the launching ramps was to be carried out by this chameleon-like unit. It is quite remarkable that, in the circumstances, Wachtel preserved his sanity. He must have remembered with rather a sour smile a conference in December 1943 when he was promised 3,000 bombs a month by April, and wondered how his depleted unit with its multifarious duties could fire such a number.

Preparations for the bombardment proceeded, and exercises to test the chain of command were carried out. By the beginning of June the Regiment was in a position to occupy all the new sites, none of which had been attacked. The only remaining anxiety was that affecting the question of supply. Air attack on the communications in France, directed to the cutting off of the German forces in Normandy, were having a major effect upon the movement of bombs.

On 6th June 65th Corps, as a result of the news of the Allied invasion, gave the order to occupy the sites. The Corps considered that six days were enough to make the ramps ready for launching, but without consulting the Regiment 65th Corps reported "readiness" on the 12th, and at 2100 hours General Jodl gave the order to open salvo fire. There were 64 launching ramps in position and, theoretically, each should have been able to despatch one bomb every half-hour. Consequently salvos of 64 could have been fired at this interval, roughly 3,000 bombs every 24 hours. What happened on June 12th was that 10 rounds were fired, of which only six were seen to travel in the direction of England. Four others were known to crash, three detonated, and one failed to explode.

The causes of failure were clear. Operation "Rumpelkammer" had depended for its initial success on the ramps being completely ready before the order to fire was given.

The original intention had been that all the ancillary launching gear should be installed on the sites by members of the Regiment and Pioneer companies. The ramps were to be assembled by the Regiment alone. For this work 10 days had been allowed, on the assumption that when the order to occupy the sites was given supplies of fuel would be available, transport would be on hand in adequate quantity and all heavy components (the bombs?) would already have been unloaded at railhead.

Because of a mistaken appreciation of the state of preparation on the sites, 65th Corps withdrew the Pioneers and cut down the time of final preparation to six days. In fact, although some gear was in position, the material and components for the assembly of the bombs, so far from being at railhead, had not even left the dumps. Further, the Regimental M.T. was below establishment strength and, in the chaotic traffic conditions produced by the Allied Interdiction Plan, was far too small to cope with the serious supply situation which quickly came to pass. The loan of 10 decrepit and unsuitable lorries from 65th Corps did nothing to improve matters, but rather added insult to injury.

It is hardly surprising that Wachtel protested violently and stated that 20th June was the earliest date on which "Rumpelkammer" could commence. His protests led nowhere. The High Command, believing that the V1 bombardment might relieve the pressure on the German forces in Normandy, insisted that the date of 12th June should be adhered to, with the results already stated.

These results vindicated Wachtel's appreciation of the situation, and again cast grave doubts on 65th Corps' efficiency. After three days, which brought the figure of the period of preparation to nearly the required 10 days, firing was resumed, though the troops were nearly exhausted by their frenzied efforts.

In the 24 hours from midday on 15th June to midday on the 16th, 244 bombs were launched from 55 ramps, 9 being still unserviceable. This figure improved day by day until on 21st June the 1,000th bomb was fired. Somewhat rested and greatly heartened by the improved rate of fire the Regiment's morale improved. By the 29th the 2,000th bomb left its ramp. This result, however, was but a fraction of the estimated possibilities and must have been a considerable disappointment to Wachtel.

Nevertheless, the Regiment received congratulations from every quarter, and the tension between it and the Corps (which was basking in the reflected glory) became outwardly considerably eased.

Wachtel seized the opportunity of improving the position of the Regiment by proposing in a memorandum to General von Axthelm that the V1 front should be extended up into Holland, and that new batteries should be formed as soon as possible. He justified this suggestion on the grounds that the wider front and multiplication of sites would greatly increase the difficulties of the enemy air forces in their endeavours to interrupt the bombardment. Further, although his existing strength was adequate for the launching of the present production of 3,000 missiles a month, it would be quite inadequate to cope with the promised flow of 8,000 a month.

He proposed that the new batteries should be formed into a second regiment, and the two made into a brigade. As the Army component of 65th Corps (the V2) did not seem likely to arrive for some time, he suggested the dissolution of 65th Corps and the placing of the new brigade directly under Luftflotte 3. It seems unlikely that this memorandum "passed through the usual channels".

While pressing for the aggrandizement of his command, Colonel Wachtel did not forget the more immediately practical necessities of the Regiment. On 22nd June a representative of the supply side of the High Command visited his headquarters and he seized the opportunity to press his needs for more bombs and more transport with which to move them.

It is only necessary to meet the Colonel once to realize how he must have striven, driven, and urged those around him in his endeavours to justify himself and General von Axthelm's choice of him as the commander of Regiment 155W. Sitting at table with him, drinking toasts in the German manner, and listening to his silences and his explosive utterances, one is soon convinced of his dedication to two causes—

that of his country and that of his Regiment, with which he was so closely associated.

His contact in June with the High Command was to have important consequences. The War Diary does not say who they were, but two representatives of the Regiment were summoned to Berchtesgaden for an interview with Hitler. For two days they were kept waiting in their lodgings, and when finally commanded to the "Presence" they had to kick their heels for 14 hours in an ante-chamber. Had Wachtel been one of the two he surely would have exploded!

At the interview Hitler was sympathetic but, on the whole, unhelpful. He would do no more than agree to the doubling of the strength of the existing regiment. No new batteries were to be formed.

Here appears one of those contradictions which occur so frequently in the history of V1. 65th Corps had realized by this time that the Colonel was building up support for himself in high quarters. At a conference on 9th July he was given authority to be solely responsible for the daily conduct of V1 operations—with, of course, conditions.

Three days later it was agreed that personnel for four new batteries should be posted to the Regiment. Hitler's decision had been negatived by a subordinate formation. In addition, it was proposed that the V1 line should be extended to the north-east, and that 64 new sites should be surveyed. Wachtel had already arranged for 32 of these to be prepared. He always seems to have been at least one jump ahead of his superiors. On 17th July instructions were received by 65th Corps, who passed the information on to the Regiment, that it had been decided to "set up immediately a second Flying Bomb Regiment". Hitler, sitting in his ivory tower, took decisions. The ordinary people lower down in the hierarchy adapted these decisions to their own desires. The German war machine was too vast to be controlled in detail by one man, and already the Führer's intuitions were suspect.

This new Regiment was given the number 255W. For the moment the chain of command was to remain the same, but the intention of the General der Flakwaffe was to form three such regiments and then amalgamate them into a brigade which, probably in accordance with Wachtel's desires, would be placed directly under Luftflotte 3.

So the Colonel's ambitions looked as though they would be realized.

On the operational front there were still many anxieties. Although success was apparent, confirmation was needed. Great attention was paid by the Intelligence Service to reports in the British Press, to news received from agents, one of whom the Regiment believed to be located in an important Ministry and, of course, from reports put out by the Embassies of neutral nations. From the tangled web woven by these stories the Regiment strove to build up a pattern of results that would justify its existence. Very recently Colonel Wachtel still believed that a million people had been evacuated from London, and that the life of the metropolis and of its government had been largely disrupted. If he had been able to put his projected programme into execution he would have been right. But many factors were against him. In the words of the War Diary the Regiment did not deceive itself as to the mounting success of the Allied defences against the bomb. The speed and altitude attained by the weapon were not so great as to prevent the fighter defence from taking an adequate toll. The improved A.A. fire, greatly assisted by the proximity fuse developed in the U.S.A., was another unexpected obstacle to success. So every effort was devoted to by-passing these two defensive measures. Opinions varied greatly at first as to whether day or night firing was the most successful from the point of view of the security of the launching crews, and of the arrival of the missile at the target. In the end it was decided, because of the flame from the engine that gave the clearest indication of the weapon's path at night, that day firing was the best, and particularly in bad weather that would hamper the Allied fighters. In consequence, on 9th July an order was issued by 65th Corps that in future no launchings were to take place during the hours of darkness.

Psychologically this may have been a mistake. The victims of VI attack, the British and Belgian people (since later Antwerp was bombarded), like their nights to be undisturbed. By day the VI attack was more tolerable, since evasive action towards air-raid shelters could quickly be taken. It is doubtful, too, if the Allied defensive measures were more effective by night than by day, in spite of the weapon's flaming tail. The civil population, nerves restored by a good night's sleep, regained their power of endurance and so, on balance, it is likely that once again the decision of 65th Corps was faulty.

During the first period of V1 bombardment the Regiment was surprised at the relative ineffectiveness of the Allies' counter-measures against the sites and the system of supply. The results of the earlier attacks on the fixed type of site had given the impression that much would have to be endured by the modified equipment. In fact, though damage was done and some redisposition of the batteries had to be carried out, the writer of the War Diary had no cause to repeat his earlier statement, made in January 1944, "that if attacks on this scale continue for another fourteen days all sites will have been destroyed". On 1st July the War Diary reports that two of the new sites have been completely destroyed, 22 have suffered heavy damage, 8 medium damage, and 10 slight damage. In the next fortnight two more sites are stated to have been completely destroyed, 16 to have suffered severe damage, 7 medium damage, and 14 slight damage in attacks in which 3,300 aircraft are estimated to have been employed.

But it was in the matter of supply that the consequences of air attack showed themselves most clearly. Transport broke down to an extent which prevented the Regiment from functioning even approximately at full capacity. In consequence there was a flood of contradictory orders as to the rate and scale of launchings, which certainly did nothing towards maintaining the effect of V1 bombardment. Thanks to the Interdiction Plan and to the assaults of the Allied long-range bomber forces on German industry, the quantity of bombs reaching the launching sites was well below the capacity of the Regiment to fire them. Expressed statistically, while the sites could have fired one bomb each every half-hour, the actual time interval was from one to one and a half hours; 80% of this time lag was attributed to shortage of supplies and only 20% to servicing difficulties, which, in themselves, were a reflection of the failure of the supply system.

V1 launching platform of the original pattern that was found too vulnerable to air attack

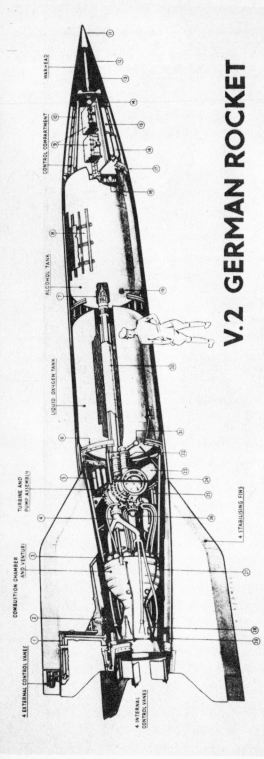

V.2 GERMAN ROCKET

1 CHAIN DRIVE TO EXTERNAL CONTROL VALVES.

2 ELECTRIC MOTOR.

3 BURNER CUPS.

4 ALCOHOL SUPPLY FROM PUMP.

5 AIR BOTTLES.

6 REAR JOINT RING AND STRONG POINT FOR TRANSPORT.

7 SERVO-OPERATE ALCOHOL OUTLET VALVE.

8 ROCKET SHELL CONSTRUCTION.

9 RADIO EQUIPMENT.

10 PIPE LEADING FROM ALCOHOL TANK TO WARHEAD.

11 NOSE PROBABLY FITTED WITH NOSE SWITCH OR OTHER DEVICE FOR OPERATING WARHEAD FUZE.

12 CONDUIT CARRYING WIRES TO NOSE OR WARHEAD.

13 CENTRAL EXPLORER TUBE.

14 ELECTRIC FUZE FOR WARHEAD.

15 PLYWOOD FRAME.

16 NITROGEN BOTTLES.

17 FRONT JOINT RING AND STRONG POINT FOR TRANSPORT.

18 PITCH AND AZIMUTH GYROS.

19 ALCOHOL FILLING POINT.

20 DOUBLE WALLED ALCOHOL DELIVERY PIPE TO PUMP.

21 OXYGEN FILLING POINT.

22 CONCERTINA CONNECTIONS.

23 HYDROGEN PEROXIDE TANK.

24 TUBULAR FRAME HOLDING TURBINE AND PUMP ASSEMBLY.

25 PERMANGANATE TANK (GAS GENERATOR UNIT BEHIND THIS TANK).

26 OXYGEN DISTRIBUTOR FROM PUMP.

27 ALCOHOL PIPES FOR SUBSIDIARY COOLING.

28 ALCOHOL INLET TO DOUBLE WALL.

29 ELECTRO HYDRAULIC SERVO MOTORS.

WARHEAD

CONTROL COMPARTMENT

ALCOHOL TANK

LIQUID OXYGEN TANK

TURBINE AND PUMP ASSEMBLY

COMBUSTION CHAMBER AND VENTURI

4 EXTERNAL CONTROL VANES

4 INTERNAL CONTROL VANES

4 STABILISING FINS

Casualties were lower than expected. Only 146 of the crews were killed, 246 wounded, and 39 were missing, presumably blown to unidentifiable shreds. Replacements came forward in excess of requirements and were added to the establishment of the batteries. Lack of manpower was certainly not one of the causes of failure.

By 7th August 1944 the Regiment began to recognize that its operations against Britain had in no way been decisive. Orders from 65th Corps indicated that the elaborate complex of firing sites in N.-W. France would shortly have to be evacuated owing to the Allied advance from the beach-heads.

Wachtel must have pondered sadly on the might-have-been. If Hitler had not vacillated over the priorities of the V programme—if Wachtel had received fuller support from above—if the bombardment had been started in December 1943 as planned—and if, above all, as he now claims, he had been allowed to direct his fire at the invasion assembly areas in south England instead of upon London, the war might have ended very differently.

Meanwhile there was much to do. Although preliminary surveys of sites in Holland had been made, the move north-eastwards, away from the advancing Allied armies, involved the transportation of a mass of equipment and material over roads and railways that were terribly damaged. The War Diary gives details of the "leapfrogging" of the various batteries from south to north but, in effect, these moves meant that only one battery remained, for the time, in action against London. It was this movement that led to the issue of the rather optimistic "hand-out" to the British Press of 8th September (Appendix I). The views expressed therein were by no means unjustified, since the planned orderly retreat of the Regiment to Holland became first a scurry and then a rout when the capture of Amiens took place. Stores and equipment had to be destroyed, the remaining "action" battery had to pull out in a hurry after having expended its few remaining bombs in a last salvo and no more than 80% of the Regiment reached its new location at Enschede, minus the majority of its equipment. The subsequent "witch-finding" conference at 65th Corps Headquarters made it clear that it was largely the wishful thinking of the Corps staff which had led to this *débâcle*.

The Corps, however, was as yet undefeated. It propounded new plans for the employment of the Regiment which took little account of the real situation in manpower and equipment of the Abteilungen. Wachtel's protests were overruled and No. 1 Abteilung was ordered to commence operations against Antwerp from the Eiffel area. Wachtel recounts that his wife— a Flemish Belgian—was at that time living in Antwerp. He was naturally concerned as to her fate, though in agreement with the military necessity of bombarding the docks through which some of the Allied armies were drawing their supplies. At the same time, he pointed out that as V1 was now intended to fulfil the rôle of long-range artillery in support of the Army, and that V2 operations had been placed under the control of S.S. General Kammler, there was no further need for 65th Corps. He advocated the placing of No. 1 and 3 Abteilungen under Army control, but 65th Corps defeated his purpose and finally maintained its position, at Wachtel's further expense. His old adversary, Oberst Walter, was given a special operational branch to control V1 operations!

In the new conditions prevailing where launchings had to take place from German territory, a considerable limitation was placed on the Regiment's functions. In France it had not mattered if a V1 misfired or turned round on its tracks to destroy a French village. But when launched from the home-land, what has aptly been described as the whimsicalities of the weapon assumed a new importance. It was therefore concluded that only a limited effort could be made from positions well to the west of the Rhine, and only one Abteilung—No. 3 —was brought into action. In addition, very special measures were taken to ensure that misfires or reciprocal tracking should not take place, with a consequent reduction in the rate of fire and the declaration of no less than 200 out of a stock of 320 bombs as unserviceable.

Flak Regiment 155W never recovered from these blows. Two of the Abteilungen were converted into light Flak batteries and No. 1 went into reserve east of the Rhine. No. 3 continued to attack Antwerp with small success. The view that the Vɪ had no independent rôle and was merely a long-range bombardment weapon for use, together with attack aircraft, in support of the Army, had completely prevailed over Wachtel's far-reaching ideas. The latter had some reward for all his hard work. Early in January 1945 he received from General Kammler a high military decoration, and three days later his bugbear Walter was posted away and he inherited the vacated appointment.

Wachtel's enthusiasm immediately revived and he formulated plans for a big Vɪ bombardment of London from Dutch sites. Fate and the Allies were against him, however. The war was drawing to a close. Soon Holland was liberated, and on the German homeland there was little scope for V operations. Wachtel, now functioning again under his pseudonym of Wolf, reorganized his batteries as infantry in the Luneberg area some time in April 1945. The Diary does not go beyond this date, and for the time being Wachtel/Wolf disappears with his regiment into the obscurity of defeat.

Today, very much alive and prosperous, he holds the post of aerodrome manager at Hamburg airport. His considerable organizing gifts and driving power are now directed to more peaceful fields.

This is the story of Vɪ from the German angle. In the next chapter the picture as seen from Britain is described.

CHAPTER VII

"THE BATTLE OF THE SITES"

BY the autumn of 1943 the coast of North-West France was bristling with threats. P.R.U.'s reconnaissances and the reports of agents showed clearly a vast activity in the construction of unusually shaped buildings, the establishment of storage depots for the assembly of some new weapon, and every indication that the enemy, even if he could not win the war, would make the cost of Allied victory as heavy as possible.

The continuous photographic cover of the French coast, of the factories suspected of making new weapons, and of Peenemünde itself, had involved photographing 7,500 square miles of enemy territory, 3,000 flights by U.S.A.F. and British P.R.U. aircraft against 100 special targets, 50 trips to Peenemünde, the taking of $1\frac{1}{4}$ million pictures, and the issue of 4 million prints. In addition, our secret agents on the continent were doing a magnificent job and their reports were flowing to Britain in great quantity. This increase in information from sources on land had been made possible by the growing strength of French resistance to the German occupation. The main theme of these reports concerned the work being carried out by slave-labour on an entirely new type of building—these had been seen to lie on an arc running from Dunkirk to Abbeville. Concrete platforms were known to exist at Siracourt, Watten, Wizernes, Marquise-Mimoyecques, and at Martinvast on the Cherbourg peninsula.

On the 28th October news was received that in the middle of the Bois Carré, ten miles north-east of Abbeville, a platform with its axis pointing to London had been discovered.

Still, it was not clear what these structures were intended to achieve. Speculation was rife about long-range guns, particularly at Marquise-Mimoyecques, but no one had a clear-cut answer to the problem.

Early in November Sir Stafford Cripps was invited by the

Prime Minister to review all the evidence about German long-range weapons, and about the middle of the month he expressed the view that there were probably four types under development. These were the gliding and radio-controlled bomb, the pilotless aircraft, a long-range rocket smaller than V2, and V2 itself. He connected the new and unexplained structures on the French coast with the launching of V1 and V2, but thought that no attack could materialize before the New Year. He recommended continued photographic cover of the French coast, and bombardment of the structures wherever and whenever possible.

On 18th November the investigation conducted by Major Sandys was brought to an end, and the Air Ministry took over all responsibility for dealing with the revenge weapons. It was, however, decided that Major Sandys' experience in the affair should still be made available to the Air Staff.

Here came on to the stage Constance Babington-Smith, an attractive and very conscientious W.A.A.F. Officer on the strength of the Photo Interpretation Unit.

It was in the Photo Interpretation Unit at Wembley that A. S. O. Babington-Smith, W.A.A.F., began her duties in the intelligence organization and it was at Medmenham that she discovered the V1.

Babington-Smith joined the W.A.A.F. in 1940 and after a year as teleprinter operator was commissioned as an Acting Section Officer for intelligence duties. Early in 1942 she was Mentioned in Despatches and, having already been promoted to Section Officer, was further advanced to Flight-Officer in February 1942. Obviously she was doing her work extremely well.

It was the task of the P.I.U. not only to reproduce vast quantities of the pictures taken by the P.R.U. aircraft, but to interpret what could be seen in these pictures in terms of military and economic intelligence, and also for the preparation of the target maps necessary to our bomber forces. The staff of P.I.U. were therefore trained to evaluate any unusual or strange object that appeared against the background of the ordinary landscape. Flight-Officer Babington-Smith had received such a training, and, in particular, she was briefed to study airfields and aircraft factories. In studying airfields she was aware that it was not sufficient to examine the landing ground itself, but because of the dispersal of aircraft and personnel practised by all the belligerents, it was essential to cover all the immediate neighbourhood. She had been warned in the autumn of 1943 to look for some form of pilotless aircraft, and when she was studying the edge of Peenemünde airfield where a road ran towards some reclamation work on the sea-shore, she saw the shadow of what appeared to be a small ramp or inclined plane. This she thought might well be a launching platform for a pilotless aircraft. As a result of her report her C.O., Douglas Kendall, instituted an all-night examination of the previous Peenemünde pictures. The ramp was detected on other pictures and after further photographs had been taken on 1st December, a cruciform object was seen lying cradled on the launching platform. This was the V1.

One of the great problems which must face those who, either as politicians or as historians, award merit to deserving individuals is to decide the relative value of the person first in the field of discovery, or that other one who, as a result of the discovery, has taken the appropriate action. In the case of Flight-Officer Babington-Smith this question arose in acute form. When the British Information Service in New York released the story of the discovery of V1, the Flight-Officer was working with the U.S.A.F. in Washington. As a result of the Press Conference that she was requested to give to the American newspapers, she was hailed as the person who had gained for the Allies the vital six months which enabled the Normandy invasion to take place without the interference of V1. Miss Babington-Smith is the first person to repudiate this suggestion. She insists that she was doing her normal work as a member of the team. What she achieved was to link the appearance of unusual structures on the north-west coast of France with the flying bomb that was to use these structures as a launching platform, and thus made clear their significance. This, in itself, was a major contribution to the protection of Britain.

As for the men and women of France who sent reports of the launching platforms, our debt to them is very heavy.

Working tirelessly and with the greatest courage, they did almost as much to breach the "West Wall" as the fighters and bombers of the Allies. Very many lost their lives, often after savage torture.

Those of us who have known the villages of the Pas de Calais have a recollection of something which is, to say the least, unpicturesque. Our infantrymen who in 1914/18 slogged in footsore agony over the cobbled roads of this region, and then spent the war winters in the mud and ice of the trenches where the names of the Menin Road, Ypres and Ploegstreet were written in the blood of those who did not return, would agree that "unpicturesque" is also an understatement. Drab, dirty, purely functional in a primitive fashion, these farms and villages were all that they would wish never to see again. But in them lived men and women of a toughened fibre. They loved their few acres of rich land, their rickety barns and their *maisons lézardées*—houses with sagging roof trees and cracked and peeling walls. When the Germans interfered with a way of life to which they had been accustomed for generations their reaction was sharp. Some—an inconspicuous few— collaborated. The majority joined the "Resistance" and, encouraged by the British, worked strongly and effectively against the enemy.

The measures taken by the Allies in the defence of the "unsinkable aircraft carrier"—Britain—were impressive. Operation "Crossbow" was launched, and in it a major part of the air forces available in the country were involved. "Bomber" Harris, as might be expected, resented any diversion from his master plan to destroy German industry and German towns. The American Air Command were also hesitant in making "Crossbow" a first priority. So the bulk of the burden fell upon the Allied Air Expeditionary Force under Air Marshal Sir Trafford Leigh-Mallory, and on Fighter Command under Air Chief Marshal Sir Roderic Hill. There was considerable dispute as to the best method of eliminating the launching sites of the two new weapons. One school of thought believed that daylight precision bombing by Americans, using the Nordern bomb sight of remarkable accuracy, would be effective. Others considered that low-level bombing by fighters would be more

successful. Both methods had their advantages, but finally the
fighter-bombers produced the best results. There is no doubt
that the overwhelming air superiority of the Allies enabled
this particular battle to be waged with a considerable degree of
success. Here the operations of the Bomber Commands of the
U.S.A. and Britain against the Reich were of fundamental
importance. As a result of the systematic destruction of
German towns a very large part of the German production of
aircraft was diverted to the fighter programme, not for the
defence of the French coast but for the protection of the
German homeland. Our fighters and bombers were therefore
able to operate successfully against the launching sites, and
their principal enemy was not the Luftwaffe, but the light and
heavy anti-aircraft weapons that guarded the coast and the
emplacements of V1, and later of V2. These defences were
increasingly handicapped by the skilful tactics employed by
our aircraft, tactics so well described in the official history, and
which are referred to later in this account.

In view of the great importance attached to the neutraliza-
tion of the sites Operation "Crossbow" was given its own
directorate in the Air Ministry and on 18th November 1943
Air Marshal Norman Bottomley, Deputy Chief of the Air
Staff, was put in charge of the battle. The attitude of the Air
Staff towards this operation may be well described as "wistful"
—full of unresolved doubts. How were these targets to be
destroyed—the large so large as to be described by General
Brereton of the U.S.A.F. as containing as much concrete as
the Great Boulder Dam in America, and the small—the ski
sites—so small as to be very hard to detect? The story of how
this was achieved is one of trial and error. It is best recounted
by giving the results of the various forms of attack described
in the operations records of the squadrons that took part—but
first detailing the methods adopted in principle by the Air
Force Commands involved. In spite of their doubts Bomber
Command of the Royal Air Force, the 8th U.S.A.F. under
General Spaatz, and the 9th Air Force under General Doolittle,
took their share in the battle. By the middle of December 1943
what became known as the "large sites" had been heavily
bombed by the fighter-bombers of Fighter Command and by

Marauders (light bombers) of the U.S. 9th Air Force, using altogether no less than 2,000 tons of bombs. The launching platforms, generally called the ski-sites because of their shape, received over 3,000 tons, dropped partly by the 2nd Tactical Air Force and partly by Bomber Command and the U.S. 8th Air Force. The technique of the attacks varied with the type of aircraft used. Generals Spaatz's and Doolittle's airmen employed, as was to be expected, the very accurate stabilized Nordern bomb sight. Bomber Command relied upon "Oboe" and Air Marshal Coningham's pilots of the 2nd Tactical Air Force on low-level raids by Mustangs, Spitfires and Mosquitos. This last form of operation was most interesting. It was the first time it had been put into effect against small targets where precision aiming was essential. The sites were for the most part in woods or small copses, and were therefore difficult to spot from aircraft flying close to the ground. But the woods themselves were easy to find, and as the sites were, for some obscure reason, not camouflaged, in the end they became a fairly simple target. If they had been built in the open fields and well camouflaged the problem of their destruction would have been much harder to solve. In the result it was found possible to bowl delayed-action bombs into the non-magnetic concrete hut that stood near each ramp and so destroy the vital element in the preparation of the V1 for its launching. In their work in detecting the importance of the huts P.R.U. and P.I.U. played an important part. It was noticed in the early photographs of the huts, the significance of which was not at that time clearly understood, that they were fitted with doors giving an opening of 22 feet. By this time it was known that V1 had a wing span of this extent so, obviously, each weapon had to be put into the hut for some final preparations before it was launched from its ramp. The destruction of the hut therefore would interfere with the firing procedure. It thus became the main objective of our assault, and it was finally decided that the tree-top method of attack by fighter-bombers was most effective against it. The storage depots were best dealt with by high-level bombing with "Tall-boys" of 12,000-lb. weight.

Now for squadron reports. First, No. 226 Squadron, equipped with Mitchell light bombers, had this story to tell:

On 4th January the squadron was detailed to attack construction site in Northern France. The bombs dropped from 5,500/7,000 feet, but the results were not good.

On 5th January we made a similar attack. A good concentration was obtained in target area and the operation was fairly successful. No enemy aircraft was seen and no flak encountered.

By 7th January no briefing was complete without those familiar words—"constructional sites!" (obviously the pilots were getting bored). This attack was fairly successful, as shown by air photographs.

On 14th January there was another inconclusive attack, but on 5th February the squadron expressed great relief at being briefed for a new target—an aerodrome at Beauvais/ Lille. The change was very welcome.

But on 6th February we were back on "constructional sites". The attack was a failure owing to cloud—the normal handicap of high bombing by visual methods.

On 8th February we made two attacks—both failures.

One attack on 9th February was believed successful, using the Gee method of radar navigation.

By 15th February the enemy was reacting vigorously. Heavy and accurate flak up to 12,000 feet was reported by aircrews.

On 24th February we made two attacks—one successful. One attack on 25th February resulted in 50% casualties from flak at 9,000 feet—but no signs of enemy aircraft.

On 28th February the attack was indecisive.

On 2nd, 3rd, 4th and 28th March there were further attacks from heights averaging 10,000 feet, but on the whole no great success. Enemy aircraft were conspicuous by their absence, thus underlining the diversion of German fighters to the protection of homeland targets—the result of Bomber Command's systematic destruction of German towns.

In April, with a vast sigh of relief, 226 Squadron went over to targets connected with the invasion of North-West France.

Meanwhile, in November 1943, Mosquitos of No. 21 Squadron had started experimenting with various forms of assault on the sites. Leaving the coast of England they flew at wave-top height and their operations book contains a number of references to aircraft hitting the sea. The first really successful attack was delivered on 22nd December by 41 aircraft of which No. 21 despatched 19. In the formation were Group Captain Pickard and Air Vice-Marshal Basil Embry who, even after his previous parachute descents in enemy territory and hazardous escapes, was still gluttonous of adventure. This operation met with very slight resistance, though the method of climbing to 2,000 ft. at the French coast and then diving on the target was soon found to be unnecessarily dangerous.

The next day the squadron was out again, but this time flak was more of a threat and a number of aircraft were damaged.

On the 31st December, and again on the 2nd January, smaller numbers were despatched. Here a new difficulty became apparent. The hedge-hopping flyers collided with flocks of birds, common at this season, and more damage was sustained.

Throughout January further raids were made whenever the weather was not so bad that, to use an Air Force expression, even the birds were walking. Various techniques were adopted, including shallow dives from 7,000 feet, but by the 17th of the month the proper method of operation was beginning to emerge. At base, a most careful study was started of photographs of the French coastline in an endeavour to establish lines of approach to the various targets that would be, as far as possible, protected from the enemy's light and heavy flak, which by this time were causing heavy casualties.

By a very careful examination of the position of these guns it was possible to decide on a line of approach that offered the enemy a target for so brief a moment that his fire would be ineffective. Flying at wave-top level aircraft could avoid being "seen" by the radar screen, and there were certain places on the coast of France which afforded a "covered way" to the objective. None of these gaps in the enemy's defence was more than 200 yards wide, so that most accurate navigation was necessary. "Gee" helped to a certain extent, but to use the graphic language of the official history, pilots and navigators of the Mosquitos were required to "paint, as it were, on the canvas of their minds, a picture of the shape and appearance of certain landmarks as seen from a low altitude". To help them the indefatigable P.R.U. aircraft took pictures of those land-marks from 50, 250 and 1,000 ft., and kept these pictures constantly available.

As an illustration of the methods employed the case of a particular site is quoted. It was found that if it was approached by flying along the left-hand side of the wood in which it was installed, the aircraft was safe. If the right-hand side was chosen —and this was where the guns were emplaced—it would most assuredly be shot down. So important was it to follow the chosen route with meticulous accuracy that if the particular gap selected was not reached at the first attempt the pilots had orders to return immediately. To fly along the coast for even a few hundred yards in an endeavour to find the gap was to court destruction.

Various other tactics were tried, including "rocketing" up to 2,000 feet from sea level when reaching the French coast, and then down again to tree-top height, thus avoiding the light flak, but the disadvantage in this manœuvre lay in the warning it gave to the radar stations even though the aircraft could only be "seen" for a few seconds. The guns near the site to be attacked would then be on the alert and fighters directed on to our aircraft.

There is an old saying among those who shoot game-birds that "They must be hit in the beak!" Birds do not mind very much having their tail feathers blown away by a charge of shot. Aircraft are more sensitive, and their tail is a vital spot. So the German gunners had an easier task, in some respects, than the sportsmen of our times, and destroyed many of our aircraft and their crews by hitting them in the tail. Squadron reports often speak of an "aircraft hit in the tail and crashing. No hope of survivors".

Throughout January the intensity of the enemy's reaction increased. Colonel Wachtel was becoming most concerned as to the possibility of launching the bombardment of Britain on the promised date. More trouble with flocks of birds was also experienced. No 464 R.A.A.F. Squadron, equipped with Venturas, had trouble with the weather, and with birds, during February. Bad conditions led to difficulty in identifying the targets, and further difficulty because aircraft, in the search for their objective, spent some time circling the area and were damaged by flak. This was on the 4th of the month. The Wing Commander leading the formation hit a tree but managed to return to base in spite of a damaged tail and mainplane. On the 9th, in view of the increase in flak, a new tactic was devised. Four minutes before reaching the coast the squadron climbed to 5,000 ft. and then dived on the target, bombing from 1,000 feet. The aircraft then climbed into cloud until the coast was reached and dived back to 1,000 ft. for the return journey. Only slight flak was experienced and, significantly, the tactic was considered "successful at the moment!"

Further attacks were made on the 11th, 12th and 13th and flak was still slight. On the 17th a "good landfall was made, target attacked successfully—no casualties". On the 24th there was more trouble with aircraft that had failed to find the target and were circling the area. One was blown up and one damaged by the bombs of other aircraft. On the 25th another successful attack resulted from the making of a good landfall and there were no casualties.

In March the Pathfinder technique developed by Bomber Command was used. The Mosquitos bombed the target indicators from 10,000 ft. with modest success. Bomber Command also took a hand during this period, but only occasionally. In January, No. 90 Squadron, equipped with Stirling four-engined bombers, varied the monotony of mine-laying off the Friesian Islands by a few "Noball"[1] attacks at night in squadron strength.

No. 100—the famous night-bomber squadron of 1914/18—attacked a site at Ligescourt by day, on the 25th June, using Pathfinder technique. "The results were excellent and no enemy aircraft were encountered." On the 29th this operation was repeated successfully at Domleger, and in July three other raids were made on the same type of target with considerable success. The real interest of these raids lies in the fact that there was no resistance whatsoever from the Luftwaffe, so deeply had the German Air Force been abased.

On 3rd August No. 427 R.C.A.F. Squadron, flying

[1] "Noball"—code-name for attacks on sites.

Halifaxes, bombed "constructional sites" in the Foret de Nieppe, using Pathfinder-cum-Master Bomber technique. On the 4th the squadron made a day attack on the Bois de Casson, and caused large explosions. On the 5th the flying bomb storage caves at St. L'Eu d'Esserent, near Paris, were hit—no enemy aircraft seen. On the 9th another flying bomb storage dump at La Neuville was raided, only partially successfully.

For a few days the squadron was diverted to other targets —how flexible is air power—and then, on the 27th, there was a daylight attack on the site at Mimoyecques. The tunnel entrance was hit. On the 28th there was a further attack on a similar dump at the Ferme de Forestet. No. 102 Squadron, also in Halifaxes, carried out the same type of operation in July and August.

But the real burden of the fight fell on the aircraft of the Allied Expeditionary Air Force, and on the 8th and 9th United States Air Forces. Altogether 18,770 aircraft attacked the sites and their storage depots, dropping 23,560 tons of bombs. The 8th Air Force neutralized thirty-five sites, the 9th thirty-nine sites, and the A.E.A.F. thirty-three. Thus the American contribution to the defeat of V weapons was very large. This enormous diversion of bomber effort from the attack on German cities and German industry may require justification. Here are some more figures.

If the efforts of Colonel Wachtel, in charge of V1 bombardment and Commanding Officer of the special Flak Regiment 155W, had not been interfered with and Hitler's intention to fire 5,000 V1 every 24 hours had borne fruit, some 600,000 flying bombs could have been launched against Britain between June and September 1944. In fact, only 5,430 were discharged, causing 6,100 deaths and injury to 17,300 people. Approximately one million houses were destroyed or damaged in Greater London. If the 600,000 V1s had arrived at their target the loss should, statistically, have been one hundred times greater, and thus would have had a marked effect upon the population and upon the direction of the war from our capital city. If these weapons had been fired at the assembly and despatch areas of our invasion forces there might have been no landing in Normandy. The war would then have dragged on for many months and might even have ended in an Allied defeat.

Add to the casualties recorded above those that were incurred by the V2 bombardment—2,800 killed and 6,250 injured—and the extent of the menace of these two weapons, if they had not been largely neutralized by our counter-measures, is very apparent.

One of the important effects of the V1 bombardment of London was the reaction of the troops serving overseas, particularly those whose families lived in the southern boroughs. The greater the distance from home, the greater the anxiety of these men. For those in France, the vast activities of the invasion precluded too much thought about suffering at home. But in the Middle and Far East, particularly among Headquarters personnel who were not actually in peril of their own lives, the first question asked at the daily news review meeting was "How many got through to London yesterday?" The flying bomb became an obsession with them, and there was a natural tendency to discount the optimistic reports of the large number brought down by our defences. Imagination boggles at what might have been the effect of the full scale attack envisaged by Hitler, and which Colonel Wachtel planned to put into execution.

For those who actually experienced the V1 attack it may be said that the winter blitz of 1940 was a very mild strain on the nerves compared with that imposed by the sounds of the approaching V1. It was the wait for the moment when the motor would stop and the weapon plunge to earth, bringing death and destruction to men and material, that racked the nerves of the population. Aircraft overhead were a fairly remote threat. A bomb fell swiftly and catastrophe was soon over. But the long-drawn-out threat of the pulsating, flaming terror that flew unrelenting across the sky was something in a quite different category of mental torture.

The effects of the V2 bombardment were purely physical. Unheard and unheralded, its explosion was the first sign of trouble, and as the fall was very scattered and the numbers relatively small, the moral effect was slight.

Though the enemy's air force played little or no part in

the "Battle of the Sites" his anti-aircraft reaction was very different. When the battle started it was estimated that for the defence of the sites in the Pas de Calais area there were deployed 60 heavy and 60 light A.A. guns. By the end of May 1944 this number had been increased to 520 heavy and 730 light weapons. The Cherbourg peninsula, always a sensitive spot for the enemy and so heavily defended, had increased its quota of heavy A.A. from 120 to 200.

This scale of flak was reported as the heaviest in Europe, and as one pilot ruefully described it, "You could almost walk on the shell-bursts!" In one attack by a large force of Marauder aircraft 160 of them out of a total of 217 were damaged by A.A. fire. The casualties suffered by the Allied Air Forces during the battle amounted to 154 aircraft and 771 aircrew, made up as follows:

8th U.S.A.F.	49 aircraft	462 aircrew
9th U.S.A.F.	30 „	148 „
British medium and light bombers	34 „	120 „
British fighter bombers	41 „	41 „
	154	771

Between the Americans and ourselves a controversy has arisen which should be resolved as soon as possible. In the official history of the U.S.A.F. in Europe the statement is made that the threat of V1 and V2 was not passed on to the United States when it first became apparent. Yet on the 27th August 1943, and again on the 7th September, Watten "large site" was attacked by the 8th Air Force and Mr. Sandys claims that the information about V1 and V2 was passed to the U.S.A. in July 1943. In spite of this the U.S.A.F. state that it was not until December of that year that they were told the real story. Apparently, according to this account, sharp words were exchanged between General Marshall and Field Marshal Sir John Dill—the British representative on the Combined Chiefs of Staff in Washington. In view of the characters of these two men it seems to be doubtful if they ever exchanged "sharp words". Nevertheless, as a result of the reports from Britain,

A British rocket being accelerated by booster rockets that drop off when burned out

V2 being hoisted on to firing platform

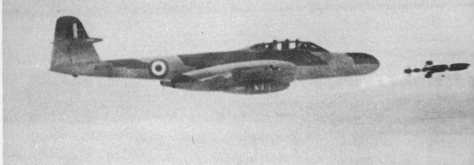

ABOVE: *Meteor Fighter firing a guided missile*

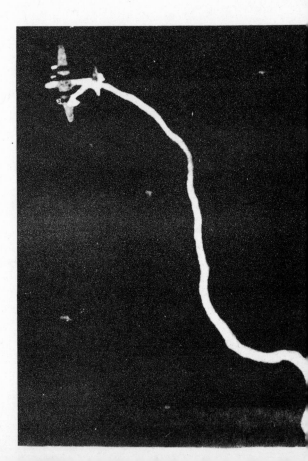

BELOW: *A guided missile tracks and strikes its target*

the occupants of the "Pentagon", that enormous building which houses the United States Military Staff, felt extremely gloomy. Their prognostications were almost defeatist. They saw "no real solution to the problem". Pay attention here, those who are inclined to underrate rocket weapons in the warfare of the future. General Arnold, the head of U.S.A.F., did not content himself with Cassandra-like pronouncements. He went into action at once. General Gardner, commanding the air base at Elgin, was ordered to make a model of a ski-site and to discover the best way of attacking it. Hardly was the concrete dry on the model site before the Air Force went into action, only to discover what the Royal Air Force had already ascertained in "hot" operations—that the fighter-bomber, flying at no feet, was the best answer.

So the battle went on. Sir Trafford Leigh-Mallory, commanding the A.E.A.F., laid down a standard of destruction for the sites. Once 60% of damage had been achieved that particular location went down to the bottom of the list—and the list was long.

By the end of May 1944, in spite of the atrocious weather during the winter and early spring which gravely handicapped the attack, no less than 103 out of 140 sites had been destroyed. From the economy angle some statistics are valuable. The U.S. 8th Air Force required to drop 160 tons of bombs to destroy one site. The Mitchells and Marauders of the 9th Air Force needed 219 tons and 180 tons respectively, while the Mosquitos of No. 2 Group, R.A.F., expended only 40 tons.

It is only human to sympathize with Colonel Wachtel, in charge of flying bomb and rocket operations. Not only was he bedevilled by the unsympathetic G.O.C. of 65th Corps to which his unit was attached, and who thought less than nothing of him and his projectiles, but no sooner had he built up his organization on the French coast than the enemy airmen proceeded to knock it down again. And to the East, in Germany, shortages of all kinds—men, material and tools— were cutting his supplies of V weapons to a point where they might cease to have a decisive influence on the war.

Here again, Bomber Command of the R.A.F., and the 8th U.S.A.F., by their attacks on German industry, were affecting the whole conduct of operations to the advantage of the Allies.

As the invasion of France continued so the threat from the V weapons was reduced. The landing sites in the Pas de Calais and the Cherbourg peninsula were overrun, and only from Holland and from dilapidated aircraft flying over the North Sea did the attack continue. It is interesting that the original platform for the launching of V1 was the aeroplane, but when Hitler demanded that 5,000 V1s should be fired as a salvo, something else had to be devised. However, at this stage in the war a number—nearly 100—of aged He 111s were pressed into the service of the flying bomb. Staggering across the North Sea with potential disaster hanging under their bottoms, the Luftwaffe pilots detailed for this job must have resigned themselves to death.

Information received by the Allies after the war indicated that as many Germans were killed by the failures of V1 when launched from the ski-sites as were casualties from Allied bombing attacks. This information must have been available to the crews of the He 111s, and only the most stout-hearted could have fulfilled their mission and launched the perilous missile—perilous to friend as well as to foe—against Britain. Waiting too for the Heinkels were the night-flying Mosquitos of Fighter Command, who claimed only a modest success against them. It is hard to intercept a target flying at sea-level. Early warning is not so easy and the sea is unsympathetic to low-flying aircraft.

V2 was a different proposition altogether. Although strenuous efforts were made to devise methods whereby it could be intercepted and destroyed or the supplies stopped, in the end what the official history calls "the drizzle of rockets" was only halted by the occupation of the territory from which they could be launched.

CHAPTER VIII

HOME DEFENCE

THE "Battle of the Sites" was, however, only a part of the activities of the Royal Air Force in its struggle against the weapons of revenge.

When the researches of Major Sandys and of the Intelligence Service had established beyond doubt that Britain was threatened by a form of attack for which there had hitherto been no precedent the whole outlook of the Headquarters Air Defence of Great Britain had to be changed. Since the early 1920s, when the possibility of an attack upon London by the French Air Force had been considered, up to the time when the real threat from Germany was established, the pattern of A.D.G.B. had not changed. Our gun, searchlight and fighter defence had been planned on the experiences of the 1914/18 war and, apart from the introduction of radar from 1935 onwards, had undergone very little modification. In 1940 these defences had given us security against the bombers of the Luftwaffe and, with varying success, had maintained this situation until June 1944.

In the autumn of 1943 a new situation had arisen. Britain was no longer threatened only by the sporadic attack of bombers and fighter-bombers from enemy-occupied territory, but by two entirely different types of weapon. The first and more remotely dangerous was a ballistic missile against which no immediate preventative could be devised, and the second was the pilotless flying bomb.

As early as July 1943 the Air Staff had considered the latter problem, including the possibility of jamming any form of radio control with which these new weapons might be operated. Our experiences in 1940/41 with the variegated means adopted by the Germans to guide their bombers by night and in bad weather to their target, pointed strongly in this direction. But no change had been made in the development of our defences where fighter aircraft were in the first line, guns in the second, and balloons in the third. In the middle of

December 1943 the Air Marshal, Sir Roderic Hill, in charge of Air Defence, was furnished with an appreciation of the threat from pilotless aircraft and was asked to plan counter-measures within the resources at his disposal. The appreciation indicated that no great reliance could be placed on these resources, in view of the probably high speed of the pilotless aircraft. If the planners had known of the basis on which the V1 had been designed—its speed in relation to an early mark of Spitfire that had fallen into German hands—they would not have been so pessimistic. Here Hitler's influence is again evident. The Führer had seen this aged and reconstructed Spitfire hopelessly outclassed by a V1 and had decided that the latter was fast enough to be invulnerable to air attack. He and others thought the same about the He 111 and Ju 88, and were wrong. He did not take into account a perfectly normal thing which his technical advisers feared to bring to his attention. In the three years that had passed not only were the new marks of Spitfire much faster, but the Tempests and Typhoons were faster still. In a desperate hurry to start the bombardment of Britain he took a chance—and lost.

Within a few days of receiving the Air Ministry appreciation the C.-in-C. Fighter Command put forward a plan. This envisaged a balloon barrage to the south of London—the probable target—and a belt of A.A. guns on the North Downs, not very far from the German objective. To the south of the gun zone would be the fighter belt reaching out over the Channel —much the same layout as the standard A.D.G.B. pattern of the previous years. In addition, Civil Defence precautions were taken on a very large scale.

There seems to be some discrepancy in the accounts of when the first flying bomb reached these shores. Some documents indicate that perhaps two landed in England about 8th June. But the official story confirmed by Colonel Wachtel himself holds that on the night of 12th June 1944, 27 V1s (Wachtel's figure is 10) were launched against us. Only four of these reached the London area, causing two fatal and some thirty other casualties. By 23rd June about 1,000 of these weapons were launched; 750 reached our coasts and 370 landed in London.

Against this attack 11 fighter squadrons, 200 heavy and 200 light A.A. guns were in action, and behind them was a screen of 500 balloons. It was the immediate intention of A.D.G.B. to increase this number to 1,000 as soon as possible.

By 29th June casualties in the London area were estimated at 1,700 killed and 10,700 injured. Many thousands of houses were destroyed or damaged. What was significant, however, was the suggestion that, so far as could be ascertained, not one bomb had been fired from the original ski-sites that had been the target of our early bomber assault. All had come from the new "modified" sites that had been so hard to find and destroy.

Our fighters found the bomb a difficult target. It was so fast that our standard aircraft had to approach in a dive in order to overtake, and by day this small object, only 22 feet in span, was hard to see. At night the flaming tail was a good indication of the whereabouts of the bomb. One of the most serious problems faced by our pilots was the estimation of the correct distance from the target at which to open fire. Long-range sniping was ineffective, and too close an approach meant the destruction, in the resulting explosion, of the fighter as well as the bomb. Some ingenious pilots flew close to the missile and, putting their own wing under that of the bomb, with a sharp lift tipped it into a nose-dive to earth. In the end, a very simple gun-sight was developed by Sir Thomas Merton, a leading scientist, and the number of kills grew very quickly.

As the month of June drew to a close so our defensive measures grew. Thirteen single-seater and nine two-seater fighter squadrons came into the battle, and every effort was made to increase the speed of our aircraft by stripping off anything that was not essential to the shooting down of the bomb. Camouflage paint was removed and all metal surfaces highly burnished to reduce drag.

By the middle of July it became clear that the original lay-out of our defences was not satisfactory. Far too many bombs were reaching London and casualties were mounting. Air Commodore Ambler, Hill's senior air staff officer, made suggestions for modifying the deployment of our aircraft and guns, and General Sir F. Pile and Air Marshal Sir Roderic Hill prepared a new plan. This involved moving the fighters' zone out to sea, and pushing our gun-defences down to the coast. A second fighter zone was allowed for in rear of the main gun-defences. By these means it was hoped that the fighters would operate more freely, that the guns would destroy the bombs much earlier, either over the sea or in less densely populated country, and that only those bombs that got through the gun zone would need the attention of the fighters in the rearward belt of defence.

Without consulting the Air Ministry, Hill and Pile put the new deployment into action. In a matter of four days, and as a result of a triumph of organization on the part of the staff, and of the most devoted work carried out by the men and women of A.D.G.B., the new layout was complete.

The reaction to this independent action was very lively. General Pile describes the operation and its consequences as follows:

"In the plain, unadorned words of Mr. Duncan Sandys describing the affair afterwards, 'About the middle of July it was decided to take the bold step of moving the entire anti-aircraft belt down to the coast. . . .' Behind this simple description of a 'bold step' there lay the story of a first-class row. The most tremendous beating of tom-toms took place. I think it was considered in some important circles that Hill had been unduly influenced by myself, or by Sandys, or by both of us into agreeing to a move which would increase our (i.e. A.A. Command) successes and decrease the R.A.F. total, which, of course, is just what it did do.

The fact was that Hill, regarding the matter less parochially against the background of civilian death and destruction, realized, as we all did, that the Air Defence of Great Britain was a combined operation, that the combined efficiency of the defences was of greater importance than the individual glory of one or other Service, that what mattered was that, somehow, the flying bombs should be mastered and it did not matter by whom.

The Air Council was very displeased. It made Air Marshal Hill fully aware of the fact that if the new move failed—and it was thought that failure was certain—he would be held responsible."

General Pile is hardly fair to the Air Ministry in this account. After all, the Chief of the Air Staff is ultimately responsible to the Cabinet for the conduct and operation of his Service, and he should have been made aware of what was proposed. It is also difficult to believe that, in reality, a question of Service *amour propre* could have been allowed to influence a decision of this importance. It must also be remembered that A.A. Command had recently become possessed of some new American equipment, notably a proximity fuse, soon to alter very considerably the results of A.A. fire which, up till then, had not been very noticeable for its effectiveness.

That Sandys, Hill and Pile were right in their decision was soon to be proved. Though at first there was a falling-off in the number of bombs destroyed, as soon as the new plan became "run-in" the number of "kills" rose most encouragingly.

By the end of July the proportion of sites in France over-run by our advancing troops had forced the enemy to take other measures. On the 18th, 19th and 20th some fifty bombs arrived unexpectedly from an easterly direction, and of these about twenty reached London. At first it was thought that a new launching site near Ostend had come into action, but soon it was found that the enemy were using aircraft as launching platforms. This development led to a further diversion of both day and night fighters from the normal deployment. Fortunately this new form of attack was soon countered by the activities of our fighters and by moving a proportion of the A.A. guns from the south to the east coast. This change was made possible by the reduction in the number of bombs fired from the north-west coast of France.

About this time the threat of V2 bombardment had become more definite, but against this weapon the only defence was attack. By the first week in August 1944 our defensive measures had reduced the scale of V1 attack to very small proportions. Less than 30% of the bombs launched penetrated the fighter/gun line, and few of these reached London. The limitations of a relatively slow robot-plane flying straight and level had enabled effective counter-measures to be taken against it. But on 8th September two rockets struck London, one in Chiswick, and the other near Epping. By 18th September twenty-five of these projectiles had reached Eastern England, and of these fifteen had landed in the London region. Our counter-measures, purely of an exploratory kind, established that the rockets came from the neighbourhood of Wassenaar, a region of pine woods and sand dunes near Leiden, from the racecourse north of The Hague, and from Walcheren Island. Our retaliation against this form of bombardment was the attack of these possible launching areas (with no great effect except the destruction of a good deal of Dutch property) and the bombing of suspected supply routes and supply depots. There was nothing more that we could do.

By the end of November over 200 rockets reached England, causing some 450 fatal casualties, of which the majority occurred in London—a rate twice as high as that inflicted by the flying bomb. This difference was in the main due to the fact that the rocket arrived without the warning which would have enabled the victims to take cover.

At home there was no means of defence against the V2. But as our armies advanced towards Germany, and as our bombers laid waste the factories in the Reich which produced the weapon, so the "drizzle of rockets" came to an end. By April 1945 it was all over, but six months earlier Sandys had given it as his opinion that "in the future the possession of superiority in long-distance rocket artillery may count for as much as superiority in naval or air power. There are signs that the Americans have already embarked upon an ambitious programme of development, and it is possible that the Russians are not far behind as they are much impressed by this new technique".

Meanwhile, conventional weapons had defeated something new which could have been most formidable if it had been brought to perfection in time. V1 and V2 in action in 1940, even in 1943, would have been decisive weapons. Fortunately for Western civilization many factors, not least the bombing of Peenemünde, conspired to delay their coming into operation. It was a close-run thing, however, and from our narrow escape we should learn, consider and devise a solution to the threat that awaits us in the immediate future.

The rockets of tomorrow will not fly for 250 miles but for 5,000. They will not be armed with warheads containing 1,200 lb. of T.N.T., but with an atomic or thermo-nuclear explosive, the power of which can only be measured in megatons, and in the reduction of hundreds of square miles of civilization into nothingness. With this threat overhanging our daily existence it is hardly surprising that in the Western world there is a certain attitude of defeatism. This attitude is by no means universal, but many ordinary people, feeling that tomorrow may be just nothingness, grab the pleasures and advantages of today. They are wrong, however, because the very fact of the existence of this threat, so universal and so all-compelling, may bring peace to the world for many generations. War is no longer the sport of kings and dictators. Its declaration means annihilation.

It may be argued that this consideration will not, of itself, prevent the occurrence of small wars, and of the type of advance by Communist countries to which we are, unfortunately, becoming accustomed. A body of opinion, very influential at the moment, can point to the Korean War, to Indo-China, and to Morocco, Tunisia and Algeria as instances of the manner in which small wars, in spite of the "Great Deterrent", can occur, and the need, in combating them, to maintain conventional forces as part of the defences of the free world. For the present this argument must be accepted, and the diversion of money and manpower involved cannot be avoided. In a later chapter some methods of keeping this expenditure within reasonable bounds are examined.

CHAPTER IX

"THE SHAPE OF THINGS"

IN the account of the "Battle of the Sites" and of Home Defence given in the previous chapters, there has been relatively little mention of the rocket—the V2. To give it the modern name this weapon was an intermediate range ballistic projectile. Its range was limited but vastly in excess of any shell fired from a gun. "Big Bertha" that shelled Paris in 1918 was a pipsqueak compared to V2, and its bursting charge of about 60 lb. was little more than what the French would call "*un pet*". Von Braun, Oberth and Dornberger had entered most successfully into a field of ballistics hitherto unexplored, and before them and their successors lies a prospect which, scientifically, is quite fascinating.

The first and most important advantage of the V2 is that, given the necessary propellant, there is practically no limit to its range. Even during the Hitler war it had touched the fringes of outer space, and in those airless regions it could fly onwards with the minimum of effort. At the height it reached it was not detected by radar of the period, and once its propellant was exhausted and it started on its downward trajectory towards its target, there was nothing in existence that could stop it, any more than a shell from a gun, if fired accurately, could be prevented from reaching its goal. Thus it was a much more powerful weapon than V1, but complicated in the extreme, and harder to produce in quantity. It could be launched from any firm surface, not necessarily a concrete platform, and it was quite indifferent, apart from range, as to the locality from which it was fired. Its launching point could be changed almost hour by hour, and the only means of stopping the "drizzle of rockets" was to capture territory, to destroy the storage depots, to block the means of transport, and finally to abolish the factories in which it was made. Altogether a long and difficult business, and a measure of the value of this new weapon which today has altered the whole conception of war, both in attack and defence.

Critics of this statement may say that, in various forms, it has been made at intervals throughout the ages. The bow and arrow altered the shape of the club and lance battle. The arquebuse replaced the bow and the gun and gunpowder replaced both. But never has there been so radical a change as that brought about by the rocket. The bow still needed almost as many archers as the spear needed spearmen. Gunpowder—to be followed by cordite—actually increased the numbers of fighting men required to operate the muskets, the cannon, the rifles and the artillery of recent years. But the rocket, and more particularly the projectile with an atomic or nuclear warhead,[1] will reduce the number of human beings that will be required to operate them, because of their immense capacity for destruction and their far-reaching striking power. This is the pattern of things to come.

One of the questions that face our military planners today is the extent to which Russia has developed the rocket weapon. We know our own shortcomings due to our laxness in the days immediately after 1945, and the advances that the United States have made in this field. The situation in Russia is obscure, but there are certain facts available which give an indication of what may be happening there.

In 1945 as the Allied forces inexorably rolled forward from west and east the German Reich was ground into the mud and dust of its own territory. Men, machines and material that had been its assets in peace and war passed under enemy control, and nowhere more fruitfully to the conqueror than in the east. In particular the organization that had produced the new weapons, V1 and V2, fell into Russian hands, and it is reasonable to expect that they have made good use of it. They are probably little behind the U.S.A. in the production of short-range guided missiles, ground to air, and air to air, and perhaps less advanced in the long-range weapons. There is still an appreciable difference between the vast technological resources of America and those of the U.S.S.R., and this is

---

[1] *Note.*—For convenience this form of weapon is referred to later as A/H, i.e. Atomic or Hydrogen warheads.

bound to be reflected in the speed of advance in producing such complicated engines. As Major Sandys stated in 1943, in his appreciation of the new weapons, "the Russians are very impressed...", and though no information has been published as to the existence of rocket weapons in Russia,[1] it would be foolish to think they do not exist, even if they are not quite up to the American standard.

Great Britain had taken little interest in rocket weapons until these threatened her with destruction. Even after the potency of this form of missile had been demonstrated beyond any doubt, there was still a clinging to the conventional forms of war that today seem little short of fantastic. The combination of the rocket and the atomic warhead should certainly have been obvious to the military mind, and yet, not only in Britain, but generally in the West, vast sums of money and a vaster physical effort have been expended in reproducing slightly improved forms of the conventional weapons that had won, with the guts of human beings to support and launch them, the Second, or Hitler, World War. Fortunately, in the background of this futility were men of science who believed that there was a way to be found leading to the point where war would destroy itself. This climax would be reached when either side in a conflict had the power to launch immediate and devastating destruction on its adversary. In fact, a case of the Irish serpents who, each swallowing the other's tail, end by eliminating the one and the other.

So far these scientists have remained in the background, and in Britain today there is this picture.

The Royal Navy have a few carriers equipped with aircraft that are manifestly obsolescent, if not obsolete. There has been talk of bringing back into operation our one modernized battleship—the *Vanguard*. The reason put forward for this view is that this is the only ship that can deal with the Russian *Sverdlov* type of heavy cruiser. Beyond these small resources the Navy has a number of very good super destroyers that are almost light cruisers and an adequate supply of anti-submarine vessels. Our submarine fleet appears to be sufficient for any

[1] Mr. Kruschev has recently (April 1956) given the world some information on this subject.

rôle that may be offered to it. Some progress has been made with short-range rockets. And all this when it seems clear that the U.S.A. Navy is well ahead with the modern weapons of war, such as long-range rockets, atomic submarines and ship to air guided missiles.

Since 1945 some senior Air Force officers have been concerned by the persistence of a policy which seems to perpetuate the ideas of the Hitler war. Medium bombers and single-seater fighters have been produced in large numbers, while an immense effort has been made to establish a tactical air force in support of army units that are obviously outdated.

Many authorities consider that single-seater fighters are dead—stone dead. They are neither useful for the interception of enemy bombers, nor will they be needed for army support because shortly there will be no army—only a police force that will need helicopters and aircraft of the Auster type for observation and transports for mobility, but nothing else that flies.

The weakness of the single-seater for interception purposes is obvious when consideration is given to the technical aspects of the problem. The bomber, with its atomic or nuclear warhead, will approach at 50/60,000 ft., and at 700 miles per hour. By the time it reaches the vicinity of its target about 40% of its fuel load, a considerable proportion of its total weight, will have been expended. Its wing loading will therefore be relatively light and its manœuvrability great. The single-seater fighter sent up to intercept it will have expended only a portion of its fuel. In proportion the fighter will be heavier than the bomber and will thus be less manœuvrable. In addition, its unfortunate pilot is faced with the problem of (1) listening to the instructions from the ground station that is trying to guide him on to the enemy; (2) trying to stay right-side-up when his aircraft is very nearly at stalling speed; and (3) reading a cathode ray tube that is showing him where the enemy—one or many—is in the sky. All this on top of wearing a "G" suit, an oxygen mask, and also watching the many instruments that are part of the routine of flying a supersonic fighter. It really does not make sense. The interceptor of the future must be a long-endurance multi-seater, manned probably by pilot, radar operator and gunner—the latter to operate the guided missiles that must be launched at the enemy bomber. No one man can deal with all these problems. It needs a well-trained team, as we found in 1941 when we first attempted night interception—with success—against the enemy bomber that was devastating our cities.

In the Army there is, on the whole, a realistic appreciation of the problem that faces the Western Allies—the N.A.T.O. powers. A certain amount of effort is being absorbed by the development of tanks, but the younger staff officers are thinking in terms of tactical atomic weapons as a preventative of "hot wars" and of the Service as a police force to control silly schoolboys in Cyprus and far more dangerous bandits in Malaya.

In the United States the progress of the armed forces towards the atomic age has been much faster. A serviceable atomic-powered submarine has already carried out an extensive cruise. Work is going ahead in the direction of making such vessels the principal striking force of the U.S. Fleet. The American Army already possesses rocket weapons and guns that can fire atomic warheads, while for many years the U.S.A.F. has been capable of delivering an atomic attack. In the background are further missiles, both guided and ballistic, that are far in advance of anything possessed by Britain.

France has one guided missile in the experimental stage. It seems to be intended as an anti-tank weapon, though this would not be the limit of its utility.

No other N.A.T.O. country has, so far, produced any of the new weapons, but no doubt research is going on in a number of places.

As this work is on the "top secret" list it is impossible to discover exactly what financial effort is being put into it. But in America it would be conservative to say that 300 million pounds are being expended this year towards the development of the 5,000-mile *accurate* rocket, with a nuclear warhead. Russia may be spending more in effort and manpower—that we can speculate about but we cannot discover. Today Britain is spending £520,000,000 on its Air Force, £475,000,000 on its Army, and £345,000,000 on its Navy. A total of over thirteen hundred million pounds. In 1912 Britain's Budget, including

defence, was about £200,000,000—at present-day equivalent
£800,000,000. This covered our total National expenditure,
including the debt service of the many small wars of the 19th
century, and the South African War, little more than half our
present expenditure on defence alone. Surely it is time to review
the whole problem presented by the needs of our armed forces,
and what the arrival of the nuclear and rocket age poses as a
question. It is not only the cost in money, but the cost in manpower which is important. In this day of over-full employment
the fact that nearly a million men and women are in service
uniform, and that another half million at least are directly
concerned—in civilian clothes—in maintaining them, gives
one, as the French would say—furiously to think. None of the
Allies, not even the Americans, have manpower to waste in
the face of Russia and the slave millions of Russian satellites.
We have got to apply our technological superiority—already
seriously threatened—to neutralizing our principal enemy's
human potential.

To illustrate this point from recent war experience a British
officer, working behind the Russian lines in the Danube zone,
reported that he saw a post of eighteen German machine-guns
overrun by Russian troops. The German gunners were brave,
and they had plenty of ammunition. They killed unnumbered
Russians, but the ant-like horde finally overbore and destroyed
them. The N.A.T.O. nations can never hope to cope with this
form of Russian strength. So we must find the technical
solution which will ensure that Russia's numerical superiority
will never prevail.

The dilemma that faces N.A.T.O. nations today is the two-
pronged—no, even a three-pronged—attack that the Communist countries are staging. First is the conventional form of
war, aircraft, guns and infantry. Here see Korea and Indo-
China. Next, the economic attack, where offers of Russian help
to under-developed nations (in spite of the Colombo plan)
always seem to be just ahead of what the Western powers are
doing, and this word "doing" is used advisedly. Finally, there
is the threat of atomic/nuclear war, carried out by long-range
rockets and supersonic bombers. This seems the end of the
road. Such a form of warfare must surely be self-destroying,

and of no advantage to either side. But it is no use adopting the defeatist attitude which some people are advocating. In 1935 the defence of Britain against the 200 m.p.h. bomber seemed difficult to achieve, and that of Malta—the vital link in the chain of Mediterranean military strength—appeared unattainable. For Malta the answer was—evacuate and abandon. But Radar provided the solution. In Malta's case the mischief of defeatism—call it realism if you will—had gone far, and we were to suffer greatly from it. But in the end success was achieved. The problem that now faces our scientists is to provide the solution to the rocket/nuclear threat. For this work they will need considerable resources—money and manpower to begin with.

Let us take a look at the £1,340,000,000 that our present inadequate defences cost us, and see how much of this vast sum can be put to the service of rocketry and the measures needed to deal with the enemy's counterpart. Some of this money is already being devoted to this end, but one may question whether it is enough. Our existing conventional forces must absorb the most of it. Pay alone takes a big slice. There does not seem to be a sufficient sense of urgency amongst our leaders. Their actions are still affected by the vested interests of manufacturers, particularly those in the aircraft industry, whose production lines are cluttered up with aeroplanes—the old-fashioned word seems appropriate—that mean money to them but no security to us. On the Army side there is still a body of opinion that thinks in terms of tanks, guns and big battalions. In the Navy there is doubt and hesitancy. Few in the Service can subscribe to the battleship theory, but some are uncertain as to the wisdom of making the carrier the capital ship, and maid of all work, of the future. To them the guided missile vessel, surface or submarine, seems a better alternative.

If then the N.A.T.O. nations—and Britain in particular—decide greatly to reduce their conventional forces and concentrate their effort on nuclear/rocket arms, in what form should this type of armament be developed? At the moment the Communist countries, Russia and China, are the only real threats to world peace. Their satellites would come into the

Western fold tomorrow (perhaps excepting Viet-Minh and Indonesia) if the two master races were defeated either militarily or politically. It then becomes a question of geography —the distance from the centres of N.A.T.O. strength to the vital areas of Russia and China.

If press reports are to be believed, the United States have already decided that their rockets must be able to travel 5,000 miles and hit their target without the intervention of radio aids—aids that in the past have been greatly open to interference. Such weapons do not yet exist. What are immediately available in small numbers are short-range weapons only tactically useful. These merely extend and develop the potential of conventional arms, and are in no sense a substitute for them. Before the strategical bomber forces and the carrier fleets can be reduced something quite new must appear—the rocket capable of carrying out strategic bombardment as effectively as the modern jet-bomber. Only the U.S.A. and perhaps Russia have made an approach to this solution.

In Britain the broad study of the rocket problem commenced effectively in 1947/48, though there were earlier burgeonings. It is to the credit of the Socialist government of the time that it agreed to establish, in the research departments of a number of aircraft firms, sections of these departments solely concerned with the development of guided missiles. So far all that has been produced is an air to air weapon. We are lagging badly. In America, though men like Dornberger and von Braun had fled there, the start was slow. But in 1953 Mr. Trevor Gardner, Assistant Air Secretary for research and development, was put in charge of the I.C.M. (Inter-continental Missile) programme, as well as the lesser rocket activities of the Navy, Army and Air Force. Today, America possesses the following useful battery of weapons. In the Air Force there is the FALCON, a light 120-lb. air to air weapon capable of destroying a modern bomber. It is carried on the intercepting fighter which acts as a platform for the missile, bringing it to within range and then releasing it. Its radar equipment then "locks" on to the target and as it is considerably faster than its victim it should have little difficulty in bringing it down. BOMARC is a more ambitious ground to air weapon which has a range of

I

several hundreds of miles and is presumably also radio-guided. NAVAHO is a first priority development. This weapon is a true guided missile of very long range, flying at atmospheric height, relatively low speed, and guided by astro-navigation. It is to use the stars to find its target. So far it must be classed as a possible more than a probable.

The Army possesses NIKE, an anti-aircraft weapon of considerable potential, but of course purely tactical in its effect. The next missile is REDSTONE, a ballistic rocket designed by von Braun and hence a descendant in the direct line of V2. It is believed to have a range of 1,500 miles and so is called an I.R.B.M. (Intermediate range ballistic missile).

CORPORAL and LITTLE JOHN are two tactical rockets. The latter can be used with an atomic warhead.

The Navy, rather naturally, is concerned in the first instance with defensive rockets and TERRIER, a small solid-fuel rocket, is already installed on a number of warships. The next development will be the offensive missile, and here the emphasis is rather on launching it from a submarine than from a surface vessel. Some naval officers consider that the surface vessel, carrier, battleship or cruiser will be too vulnerable in a future war and their thoughts turn to the invisible and unsuspected submarine, creeping undetected towards the enemy coast. At the appropriate moment it will establish its position by secret methods, and then, still submerged, launch its guided atomic weapons at the enemy's cities.

In the Caribbean, at Patrick Base in Florida, the world's largest firing range—some 4,500 miles of sea—is being opened. There the Americans intend to test their I.C.B.M. and a variety of shorter-range weapons. The measure of the urgency with which they are working lies in their anxiety to answer the question as to which nation—Russia or America—shall lead in the race to perfect these weapons. There is a real fear in official circles that Russia may have moved ahead in this struggle, and that one day not far distant a Russian I.C.B.M. may land near America's shores, to be followed by a summons to the N.A.T.O. governments to a conference at Moscow where the terms of surrender will be dictated under the threat of universal atomic/nuclear bombardment. By comparison with the

American effort, and indeed if we are to believe French propaganda, even that of France, Britain lags far behind. From the financial and manpower aspect this is probably true, but technically it is not unreasonable to question this view. The fact remains, however, that in Britain the only information about rocket weapons hitherto published refers to an air to air missile, presumably on the lines of the American FALCON. It has also been stated that we are prepared to use tactical atomic weapons as well. Apart, however, from what we could borrow from the Americans, this seems in the nature of an empty threat. There is no information at all about British counterparts of the atomic gun, or the CORPORAL rocket, and certainly none of them are as yet in service with the Army, though it has been reported that the War Office has bought some examples of CORPORAL.

It seems that the Navy will have in operation by 1957 a short-range anti-aircraft rocket, but of more ambitious weapons there is no news.

It would be very heartening to be told that the problem of the future war is being tackled with a full appreciation of what can be achieved with guided missiles.

What then are the reductions in conventional arms that can lead to greater effort in rockets? And what kind of security can be achieved by such a development?

Before any attempt is made to answer these questions it is as well to see what Britain's armed forces are planning for the future, as opposed to what they possess at the moment.

In the Navy Estimates issued this spring (1956) great emphasis is laid on the use of atomic energy as the motive power of submarines and on guided missiles as the offensive and defensive weapons in surface vessels. The carrier is regarded as the capital ship of the future and four types of aircraft are being developed for its use. Anti-submarine frigates take pride of place in the building programme, and here, once again, conventional planning is evident. Perhaps this is only an interim measure until the inter-continental guided missile can determine the future of enemy submarines beyond doubt, by destroying their bases and harbours in the first hours of the war. Nevertheless, money and manpower is to be spent on the production of these frigates, and the Reserve Fleet, modified to meet modern requirements, will absorb a considerable part of the naval resources that are available. These estimates represent the compromise that results from the great uncertainty that envelops the rôle of the Royal Navy in the future.

The bold move of depending on carrier task-forces, equipped with medium-range missiles to supplement the long-range bombardment from land bases, and on submarines equipped with similar weapons capable of being fired while they are submerged, seems only remotely in contemplation. The Navy still thinks in terms of the surface battle at sea against an enemy cruiser force such as is possessed by Russia, and of the anti-submarine struggle in the protection of our trade. Perhaps such battles will again take place, but their successful conclusion must depend on the whole-hearted support of the United States fleets. Otherwise the balance of numbers, and hence the probable result, is entirely against us.

It may be that behind the scenes there is work of a more profitable nature well in hand, but every part of our resources in cash and manpower that is diverted to obsolescent weapons must delay very badly the day when the Navy can be regarded once more as an up-to-date and really valuable adjunct to our national defences.

The Army Estimates 1956/57 certainly take into account the double threat under which we live—the creation of unrest all over the world that is inspired from Moscow, and the threat of atomic/nuclear warfare. To deal with the first a highly mobile, hard-hitting force is being organized, ready to fly to any potential danger spot and smother the first smoulderings of a small war. In the rest of the Army a realistic attitude is being adopted towards the use of tactical atomic weapons. The hypocritical idea that we should not be the first to fire an atomic rocket has at last been abandoned, and such a weapon is coming to be regarded as part of the normal armoury of a modern fighting force. So far so good. There are the beginnings of a police force such as the future will require, and the new weapons are moving forward in the list of priorities. But the vast "tail" of administrative and non-combatant units that are still required to meet our immediate "conventional" necessities is an immense drain on our national resources. The sooner this "tail" is docked the better for us in every respect.

In the Air Force Estimates for 1956/57 there is an atmosphere of doubt and indecision. The whole fighter programme is in the melting pot. Compelled by the vested interests of the aircraft industry and by the programmes of construction based on the experiences of the Hitler war, our squadrons are equipped with single-seater fighters that the pilots themselves consider will be no use in a future war. The day of the single-seater is gone. No one man can master the complexity of the task involved in flying a supersonic machine at 60,000 ft. and more, in attending to the instructions from the ground control station, in watching his radar which is to show him his position relative to the approaching enemy, and finally, in launching his guided missile at the target. The aircraft gun is as dead as the Dodo. The Aden cannon and its associates could be scrapped tomorrow with no loss in our security. So the guided air to air missile, as the estimates admit, must take the place of the gun. The fighter of the future must be at least a two-seater, preferably a three-seater, carrying pilot, radar operator and missile-launcher, though the two latter rôles might be combined if a satisfactory mechanical substitute could be found to do the work of one of them effectively. Unfortunately it is very doubtful if our only two-seater, the Javelin, has the performance or the endurance to be a satisfactory launching platform for the new missiles.

On every hand therefore the need to move towards "rocketry" as a solution to our problems is very apparent. The short-range interceptor fighter seems useless. A ground to air missile can take its place. A long-range multi-seater for local interception may still be useful, and as an escort for our V-bombers would have a part to play. As regards the V-bombers, their position is already threatened by the I.C.B.M. and the 5,000-mile guided missile. Since these two rocket weapons are still very much in the experimental stage the V-bombers will survive for some years. But on the grounds of cost alone their numbers should be strictly limited. Each V-bomber with an atomic/nuclear bomb is the equivalent of 2,000 conventional aircraft carrying 10 tons of high explosive. Hence a modern bomber force of 50 V's may well be able in one attack to produce the results that the Bomber Command of 1945 took a year to achieve.

This is the scale of the problem with which we are faced today, and upon the correct answer being given to the many questions that arise from it will depend the security of Western civilization.

CHAPTER X

N.A.T.O. STRATEGY

INTO any attempt to answer these questions there must enter a great deal of speculation. But by starting from known facts and analysing the extent to which N.A.T.O. is already committed to certain lines of action, it is possible to arrive at some conclusions that may well be valid.

War has always been a matter of geography, and the war of the future will certainly be fought on this basis. Distances, vulnerable points, seaways and airways will determine the military policies of both sides. Population will come into the problem as well, and nationalism is already an important factor, so important that it seems worthwhile to give it first place in this analysis.

When in 1945 hostilities in Europe came to an end, Russia disclosed her aggressive intention. The problem thus posed to the Western Allies tended to obscure a threat that was already reaching formidable proportions. Nationalism was taking a hold in a number of areas where the Allies believed they held secure bases. In North Africa, in India, Burma, Malaya and Indo-China, this movement was well advanced. But with Russia on the march, the immediate difficulty had to be faced, and through the North Atlantic Treaty Organization the West started to rebuild its military strength. In America the theory of a global air strategy had gained many followers and the U.S. Air Force had maintained its Strategic Bomber Command at great strength. In consequence, and as part of N.A.T.O.'s defensive measures, the United States undertook the creation of a series of airfields in many parts of the world, including North Africa. At the time Morocco and Algeria seemed firmly in the hands of France, and Britain appeared well established in Egypt and Jordan. Palestine had been abandoned under pressure from the Unites States, but British Air Forces were still in Iraq.

Thus the United States air strategy based itself on its

ability to operate aircraft on an arc extending from Alaska across the North American continent, through Iceland, the United Kingdom, Western Europe, North Africa, the Middle East, and as far as Japan.

A large gap existed, and still exists in India, due to the British withdrawal and Mr. Nehru's neutralist policy, but there is little that can be done about it.

On this chain of air bases a vast effort in men, money and materials has been expended. Now, owing to the rise of nationalism in important sections of this chain, a considerable part of the structure appears to be crumbling.

Curiously enough, America is in some measure responsible for this damage. Both during and after the war her anti-colonial policy was directed against those of her Allies who possessed colonies. Soon Holland, France and Britain were to lose territory in the East which they had firmly held for many years, and with their loss went a measure of Western security. Later, the upsurge of nationalism spread to North Africa. Today the position in the Mediterranean is such that the protection of the bases in that area upon which the operations of the N.A.T.O. sea, land and air forces stationed there must depend is becoming increasingly difficult. This threat is at present being met in a conventional manner by pouring troops into the disaffected regions in an attempt to restore order, at the expense of the measures thought necessary to maintain Western defence against Russian aggression. For example, nearly half the French Army is now in North Africa, and a greater part of the troops intended to provide the British strategic reserve in the United Kingdom is now in Cyprus. The same sort of situation prevails in Malaya, where the defence forces are now asking for troops from Australia as well as further reinforcements from the U.K.

What will be the solution of these problems of insurgent nationalism is still a matter of doubt, but in any event, the existence of N.A.T.O. bases in these territories is not only threatened but almost certainly of short endurance. Some other policy than that of the encirclement of Russia with a string of strategically placed airfields, suitable for the operation of an obsolescent air force, must be evolved.

The recruitment of troops for the conventional arms is closely connected with the problem of population. In the past it has been possible, through the medium of conscription, to maintain the armed services at the strength required in war. Some nations, especially those in Europe, have maintained their peace-time forces in the same manner. Britain has come to compulsory service in peace-time with great regret, and small success. Today she is already planning to abolish conscription as soon as the volunteer element can be built up to the required strength. Unfortunately, the possibility of achieving this aim, with the numbers required by conventional methods of warfare, seems remote.

At the present rate of progress the voluntary enlistment of the 650,000 men and women required—110,000 for the Navy, 240,000 for the Royal Air Force, and 300,000 for the Army— will take unnumbered years.

Consider the different situation in Russia and her satellites. With a total population approaching 240 million, and with absolute authority to conscript and train numbers vastly in excess of what the N.A.T.O. powers can raise, she must always be well ahead in the manpower side of the arms race.

Finally, there is the over-riding question of finance. Figures have already been given of the astronomical cost of our conventional forces, and of course the same sort of budget applies to other member nations of N.A.T.O. Russia's success in undermining the military position by her support of Nationalism is only equalled by her triumph in the financial field. Practically every N.A.T.O. nation is groaning under a burden of taxation unparalleled in peace-time, and the seeds of communism are sprouting fast in the soil of discontent.

Surely in this atomic/nuclear age such a conception of warfare is out of date. We should be thinking mainly in terms of the "Great Deterrent"—the atomic/nuclear bomb—and not as though we were still tied to the weapons and methods of the Hitler war. Russia must be highly delighted at the success of her efforts in breaking down at least some part of the Western defences. Her attitude at Geneva seemed clearly to reflect her satisfaction in the military situation as it exists today.

To disillusion her and get back to a position where we can

dictate and not be dictated to, an entirely different approach should be made. We must consider whether we need to be strong everywhere—whether we must control all the approaches to Russia, and all the avenues along which our forces must move and trade flow. It is necessary to face the fact that it is only the "Great Deterrent" that will preserve peace and prevent Russia from continuing her military efforts to establish world communism. And let us all realize that war against Russia, if it comes, must be total—atomic and nuclear—and will be over in a very few days. Then Russia's masses will never have a chance to move, and well she knows that if the West is determined to go straight to total war, her game is not worth playing. So, there should be a complete re-examination of the West's strategy, basing all consideration on the theory that the only major war necessary to plan for is the atomic/nuclear struggle. The West can then afford to concentrate its principal forces in territories which are demonstrably secure, and, further, to effect considerable economies and achieve an increased efficiency by so doing. The new bombs can be delivered effectively from our own territories—Canada, U.S.A., Northern Europe, and Britain, and the American-held islands around Japan.

It may be argued that if the N.A.T.O. powers withdraw from areas where nationalism is threatening local security, Russia may well step in to fill the vacuum thus caused. Egypt already seems to be a case in point. But even here it is doubtful whether Russia will do more than gain goodwill and economic concessions. The Egyptians are unlikely to let King Stork take the place of King Log. The argument that on account of the vast destructive power of the A/H weapon we must maintain the maximum number of bases from which to launch our own attack, does not seem very compelling when consideration is given to the immense land areas of Canada, U.S.A. and Western Europe. In addition the atomic- and rocket-equipped submarine can fill any gap that may be of a serious nature. This then appears to be the only objection to withdrawal and it is not too overwhelming.

On the other hand, there would be considerable propaganda value in abandoning such bases. It would be possible to bring moral pressure on Russia to evacuate the satellite countries as a *quid pro quo*. Whether she would do so is another matter, but at least it would throw her on the defensive.

We can forget much that is concerning us today if we really take the trouble to understand the true meaning of the war that may be just ahead of us. We shall not have to bother about protecting our sea communications over a long period, nor shall we need to move great armies or vast masses of material. All that we shall require will be a concentration of suitable airborne weapons, including rockets, submarines and guided-missile ships that will carry the destructive force of the "H" and "A" bombs into the heart of the enemy's territory, with a police force for local population control. If we do this quickly and effectively we shall save ourselves. So let us build our forces on the right lines and no longer waste time and effort as we are doing today.

Before leaving this most important subject there is one other aspect that seems worthy of consideration. In the press of the world mention has been made of the *tactical* use of atomic missiles by N.A.T.O. to offset the Russian numerical superiority.

. When we take into account the range of the new rocket weapons the absurdity of talking in terms of tactical and strategical bombardment becomes apparent. The rocket and its A/H warhead have merged the two into one. It seems now that a strategical offensive must be that of the mind—something that ignores distance since it is a spiritual matter. The war of the future is then likely to be waged by the tactical offensive against the bodies and artifacts of the enemy, and the strategical offensive directed against their minds by means of propaganda. The manner in which this propaganda should be conducted can well be deduced from the past history of "The War of Ideas".

When the 1914/18 war broke out neither the civil nor the military departments of the British Government had any conception that there would be a very great need to explain to the neutral nations the aims of the Allies in their conflict with Germany, nor that through the medium of the press and wireless bulletins it would be possible to attack not only the morale of the enemy's civil population, but that of his armed forces as well.

For the first years of the war, Britain and her Allies concerned themselves mainly with maintaining the courage and endurance of their own nationals by some exaggeration of good news, and by the suppression, through censorship, of bad news and defeatist ideas. The press was very severely controlled under the instructions of the security departments of the Admiralty and War Office. The papers, starved of factual material, seized on every rumour such as the famous story of Russian troops landing in Scotland in mid-summer with snow still sticking to their boots.

Such a situation obviously could not be maintained indefinitely, and gradually the demands of the great press lords, Northcliffe, Rothermere and Beaverbrook, began to break down the resistance of the military departments to the use of newspapers as a weapon of war.

On 21st February 1918 the Ministry of Information was created under the guidance of Lord Beaverbrook, and later in 1918 a further step forward was taken. Lord Northcliffe was invited by Mr. Lloyd George—the Prime Minister—to become Minister for War Propaganda.

Through the medium of the newspapers he controlled and by contributions from skilled writers such as H. G. Wells, Wickham Steed, R. W. Seton-Watson, and Captain Chalmers Mitchell, Northcliffe fed the enemy and the neutrals with news which, though factual, was angled to support the Allied cause and injure that of the enemy.

The staff work required by this campaign was carried out at Crewe House in Curzon Street, which the Marquis of Crewe had placed at Lord Northcliffe's disposal. Accommodation for the staff was thus acquired for nothing, and all told, the cost of the department and its work was kept at a very low level. But before the new Ministry came into being the War Office Intelligence staff, under the direction of Lieut.-General Sir G. Macdonough, had formed a small propaganda branch which, in the spring of 1916, prepared leaflets which were to be dropped by aircraft over the enemy lines. The importance of this work grew until in early 1918 as many as a million leaflets had been dropped. By this time the German troops were, as a whole, very tired of the blood, mud and cold of a war which seemed to lead them nowhere, and the leaflets had some effect. The German General Staff were disturbed to the point of threatening reprisals against the Allied leaflet-droppers and, in one case, carried out their threats. Weakly the Allied General Staff decided to abandon this quite legitimate method of warfare, and when Lord Northcliffe took over he was faced with a situation in which one of his most potent weapons was denied him. In spite of vigorous representations leaflet-dropping from aircraft was not resumed until the autumn of 1918. Attempts were made to use balloons for the purpose, and, thanks to the prevailing westerly winds that blew them over German territory, these efforts were reasonably effective. The leaflets were also fired by various weapons from the Allied trenches. It must be remembered that the activities of Crewe House commenced a year after the Russian collapse and only a few weeks before the Allied defeat on the Somme in March 1918. Conditions were therefore extremely unfavourable to the propaganda campaign. Nevertheless, as the front line in France became stabilized and news of victory in the east was added to the hopes raised by the arrival of American troops in Europe, the battle of words gained volume and momentum. Nations that for a while had been convinced of Germany's ultimate success began to waver, and finally decided to join the winning side. In Germany the civil population was affected to the point where admirals and generals could say, with some justice, that they had not been defeated on sea or land, but by the collapse of civilian morale.

Lord Northcliffe's successful policy was based on a correct evaluation of the character and mental processes of the German people. He believed that good psychological warfare must keep well ahead of events. He considered that it should act as a pacemaker to policy, and should mould public opinion without seeming to do so. His skill in achieving these objects is referred to very appreciatively by the German Commander-in-Chief of 1918, General Ludendorff, in his memoirs published shortly after the war.

Northcliffe admitted that "every Allied victory that brought the war aims nearer of attainment enhanced the value of propaganda", and he maintained that the campaign should always give the enemy "something to hope for and much to fear".

Of course there were many other factors such as the victory of August 1918, and the Allied blockade that produced near-starvation amongst the common folk of the Reich, but propaganda played a very large part. When peace returned the whole mechanism that Northcliffe had created, and which had cost under £100,000 in direct expense, ceased to exist. But the lesson had been learned in Britain. Before the Hitler war broke out plans had been laid and on mobilization the Ministry of Information and the Psychological War Executive came into being. At first our propaganda was largely ineffective. The Germans were climbing to the heights of their success and were flushed with triumph. The pamphlets dropped over Germany in the period of the "phoney war" were just so much waste paper, and the broadcasts to Europe had very little influence.

Gradually, however, the constant iteration of Allied propaganda, particularly the news service, began to have its effect. The news from the B.B.C. came to be regarded, with some justice, as the truth and the enslaved peoples, listening at the peril of their lives, hung on the words of our announcers as though they were directly inspired from Heaven. Even the German people began to listen to the B.B.C. and studied the neutral press—so limited in comparison with 1914/18—with close attention.

As an illustration of the anxiety induced by this development in the minds of the German Propaganda and security staff, a radio commentary, probably given by the renegade Englishman Joyce, generally known as Lord Haw-Haw, is quoted. This talk was in answer to one of the regular Air Ministry broadcasts given towards the end of the Battle of Britain. The points made in this broadcast are also quoted, as follows:

"It is three weeks since I last spoke to you and there has been no invasion, except from the skies, and that mainly at night. The German Air Force appears to have accepted the position that without the cover of a very large force of fighters or of dense cloud, they cannot send their bombers inland by day. As far as we can see, a very high proportion of the bomber force has been turned over to night operations, and indeed, the scale of night attack by these bombers begins to approach that of the earlier attempts by day. The fighter force is being used almost exclusively in tip-and-run raids across Kent and towards London, flying at a very great height, over 30,000 feet in some cases, but occasionally lower when these fighters are carrying bombs.

This tip-and-run raiding is irritating and dangerous to us but, owing to the small scale of attack, it can never be decisive. It is really an attempt to wear down our fighter force and the nerves of our civil population by constant pin-pricking. The idea is that the continual air raid warnings and the occasional explosion of bombs will upset and disorganize us.

The night bombing, of course, does more damage, and is a more serious problem, which we are doing our best to solve. I wish the German High Command could see a little greengrocer's shop somewhere in this city. It has been knocked out but the owner still goes to market to buy his cabbages, the fruit which comes to us so regularly from overseas, and his other wares. He spreads them on a stall outside the ruins of his premises and at the stall is the following notice: 'Don't worry about this—we are carrying on. Our branch business in Berlin is in a very much worse state!' This is the kind of spirit which makes me so confident in the result of the war."

Lord Haw-Haw replied as follows:

"Air Marshal Sir Philip Joubert was recently required to broadcast on the situation of the war in the air, evidently with a view to reassuring the British public. Certain misgivings and doubts must have been spreading in Britain relating to broadcasts of what is believed to be the news by the B.B.C., and so that the Air Marshal himself had to step into the breach. He did so with a peculiar grace all his own, rather clumsily admitting a number of things which, so far, official British sources had been painstakingly careful to conceal, and rather unconvincingly claiming strength where weakness is very evident.

In speaking of the tactics of the Luftwaffe, the Air Marshal presented the recent change in the method of German daylight raids, now largely carried out by fighter-bombers instead of heavier and slower aircraft, as favourable for Britain. He asserted that evidently Germany was not able to send heavy bombers to England by day without a heavy fighter escort, or at least an 'overcast' in which to take refuge. But does a change of tactics imply that one is no longer able to pursue methods first employed?

Is it not at least as probable that it has not become possible to employ better means of attaining one's objective, and that the change of tactics is one of entirely free choice? The Luftwaffe is using different methods because they are more effective. That, of course, is too simple an explanation for Sir Philip to give. He prefers to make a clumsy attempt to imply that some dark, mysterious force, operating in support of the R.A.F., has compelled the Luftwaffe to change its tactics from good to bad. But Londoners themselves will best be able to judge whether the present tactics are more effective or not. That this is so is quite evident from the Air Marshal's admission that, of course, these daylight raids were a great strain on the London population. By admitting that Sir Philip Joubert hopes to make Londoners believe that that is their only effect. If it were, the Luftwaffe, which aims at destroying military objectives, would most certainly not have considered the change of tactics worthwhile. A mere nuisance value is not enough for the forces of Reich-Marshal Goering.

While joking about a London greengrocer who continued to sell his wares on the ruins of his shop and showed that he had not lost his sense of humour by displaying a notice 'I wish you could see my Berlin branch', Sir Philip Joubert attempted, with the delicate tread of a hippopotamus, to imply that greengrocers' shops in Berlin were in an even worse condition. We are not at the moment quite sure whether, among the houses hit by the R.A.F. in Berlin, there is a greengrocers' shop or not, but we do know there was no factory or warehouse, or objective of military importance in any way materially affected, and that, after all, is the most important point. One can go on selling cabbages if one has them on the ruins of one's shop,

Booster rockets at the end of their run are burned out and then detach themselves from the missile which then flies on under its own power

The United
States Air Force
"Snark" long-
range missile

but one certainly can't turn out any Hurricanes or Spit-fires on the ruins of an aircraft factory. And that such factories are most accurately hit by the German bombs was a point most significantly admitted by the Air Marshal. That the British aircraft industry has long ago given up all hope of catching up with Germany's figures in aircraft production and thus gaining air supremacy, was another fact which transpired during Sir Philip's broadcast. He consoled listeners by stressing that American deliveries of aircraft would have enormously increased by next spring and implored them to hold out with confidence until that time. Nothing was said of the British factories which, according to other official British sources, are to play such a decisive part in winning the war.

Germany's daily losses

Sir Philip Joubert, singularly, made no mention of any new and wonderful methods which are just in the process of being perfected by which German night raids would be stopped. All he could say was that these German raids were so costly that they would cease of their own accord one day. It is difficult to see how it is to be the case if the Luftwaffe loses only half a dozen or so aircraft a day. Even if, for argument's sake, we adopt the British figures, the absurd reports of 180 or more German planes shot down might, if they were believed, have created the impression that the German raids were costly affairs. But if even the B.B.C. claims only half a dozen German planes as the day's bag, well, Sir Philip Joubert will find it difficult to persuade his listeners that the German raids are so costly as to cause the Reich-Marshal to desist of his own accord. Besides, what about all this talk of taking the initiative and resorting to an offensive? If all Sir Philip can do is to ask the British people to wait until the Reich-Marshal decides that they have had enough, then he might as well have thrown up the sponge at the beginning.

There were a good many other points in Sir Philip's broadcast inviting comment, but these seem to us to be the more important ones. Perhaps, however, it will have interested those who believe that the Spitfires and Hurricanes were superior in performance to anything that

K

the Luftwaffe could muster to hear that plans have already been made to give them a heavier armament, and make them faster, as well as to design altogether a new and superior type. We did point out, you know, quite a good while ago, that the Messerschmitts, having cannon, were more heavily armed and also a good bit faster than the British fighters. So there you are.

Finally, Sir Philip did make excuses for the less violent anti-aircraft fire over London. He did say that this, of course, was only to lure the planes of the Luftwaffe to more certain destruction, and not to save ammunition. But why then have so few German planes fallen into the cunning trap? We hope you will pardon us for wondering."

Today this may seem rather poor stuff, but at this time there were reports of criticism in Britain as to the truth of the Air Ministry News Service. The public were very ignorant on air matters, and since there was little other news of interest available at the time, there was a tendency towards boredom at the wealth of reports on air operations, and of a feeling of doubt as to their accuracy. Many hundreds of thousands were accustomed to listen to Lord Haw-Haw and his talks were striking home.

Thus on both sides of the English Channel propaganda was becoming increasingly effective. On the whole, however, that coming from Britain had the better results, particularly when it became more and more obvious that, as the consequence of Allied successes, Germany's chance of winning the war was fading.

The Japanese were tougher. The considerable organization known as the Far Eastern Bureau, that was established by the Ministry of Information in Delhi, beamed its broadcasts and scattered its pamphlets with negligible effect. Not until real success attended the Allied operations did Psychological Warfare (commonly known in the Services as P/W) achieve any results, and then there was only a slight softening in the resistance of the Japanese armed forces. The number of Japanese soldiers that surrendered owing to the influence of our operational P.W. units, broadcasting from close behind our firing line, was very small. No better subject for psychological attack could—apparently—have been found than these emaciated, diseased, and dispirited troops, but they did not give in, such was their faith in themselves and in the teaching that they had received in their homes. As the war progressed P.W. may have influenced the more intelligent people both in Germany and Japan. Certainly in Germany there was built up the movement that ended in the attempted assassination of Hitler, and, consequent on its failure, the death of a number of the more astute leaders. In Japan many people were thinking of surrender even before the first atom bomb was dropped on Hiroshima.

Today in Britain there is little left of the organization that contributed to the Allied victory. The Ministry of Information has been replaced by the Central Office of Information where a number of devoted people blow upon the dying embers of P.W. Britain's point of view, her motives and intentions, are put forth with praiseworthy zeal by the C.O.I., but they produce hardly a ripple on the surface of world opinion.

Against this sombre background the flamboyancy of Nasser's polemics, the impertinences from Athens, and the supremely skilful propaganda from the Kremlin, shine like stars in an inky firmament. We are spending from fourteen to fifteen hundred million pounds on armaments that may never be called into use. On the weapon that can be used from day to day—the spoken and written word—our budget is just a few million. This includes all the cost of the C.O.I., the British Council, and of the B.B.C.'s overseas service.

As the rocket and the A/H bomb have vastly extended the striking power of the armed forces, so have radio, television and the modern press increased the range of national propaganda. Clearly then we must apply men, money and effort towards maintaining a balance between physical forces such as the present navy, army, and air force, and the forces of the mind that are constituted by the press, radio and television. The more we develop these latter powers in peace-time, the better we shall be placed, both defensively and offensively, if war—hot war—should come.

There is at present a great deal of opposition on the part of some newspapers to the modest efforts that the British Council makes to publicize the British way of life abroad, and it may be thought that this opposition would become more violent if larger funds were made available for what is in fact a very potent form of psychological warfare. Nevertheless, much more could be achieved than is at present possible, particularly if the responsible papers were taken into the confidence of the authorities rather more amply than is at present the case.

There is a certain type of functionary, brought up on the doctrines that pertained in the Victorian era, who regards the press as a natural enemy. The sooner this type disappears from public life the better for the national health. In the U.S.A. the press has direct access to the President, and lesser lights live for and by newspaper publicity. Such an extreme development is unlikely to suit our national character, but there is a long way to go from the present handling of reporters in Britain, and the profitable co-operation that might be achieved by a more liberal outlook towards publicity. What if an occasional difficulty arose? The sum of credits would greatly outweigh the few debits.

In peace-time it must be admitted that little reliance can be placed upon a considerable section of the popular press to propagate the official view. However anxious the Government may be to follow a certain line of argument in its publicity to foreigners, the fact remains that newspapers, in the main, are run by private enterprise that is concerned with the profit motive. Hence the printed word must be interesting, amusing and, above all, saleable. Much of the information which a government may wish to reach a wide public lacks that spice which a spoiled population has come to regard as its right. Nevertheless, the majority of British national and local newspapers, though they have a lively preoccupation with the need to pay their way, are prepared to "slant" their material in a manner favourable to the national interest.

But, in spite of what many Service men and some civil servants still think, it is not enough to distribute a "hand-out" (a piece of government information) to the press and so ensure its publication. Unless it has some news value it goes straight into the waste-paper basket.

Governments, other than those of the police states, must

therefore regard the press as an occasionally useful ally, but not as the sole vehicle for the dissemination of propaganda.

Radio and television are in a slightly different position. Usually they have been dependent for their creation, though not for their continued existence, on government support. They are, in consequence, rather more malleable than the press, and as their impact on the public is immediate and widespread the influence that they can exert, as a propaganda medium, is immense. Anyone who has sat in the duty officer's room at the B.B.C. after a controversial programme can subscribe to the immediacy and effectiveness of radio. Telephone calls arrive at minute intervals, some from admirers, many from dissentients, but all from people whose interest has been evoked.

This interest can be very great amongst the illiterate. In Middle Eastern and Far Eastern countries the written word goes for little because so few can read. But round a ramshackle fourth- or fifth-hand radio set a group of Arabs, Sudanese or Negroes can sit and soak in the vicious anti-European programmes from Cairo Radio.

By means of the information services that are under their control governments can and do produce results favourable to their policies. It is not suggested that the rabble-rousing tactics of countries like Egypt should be followed in the West. But the reading-room, the news letter, the film, the broadcast, and the wandering lecturer, can and do produce results. The visits of cultural organizations under government auspices, such as ballets, orchestras and the theatre, can add materially to the total effect.

So far, all this has been very haphazard because no one at the top seems to have a very clear idea of what is to be achieved—except Russia.

If then, in the rocket/nuclear weapon age, propaganda is to be regarded—as it should be—as a primary method of maintaining policies, each government should regard its control and organization as one of its major concerns. What is actually happening is very different. In not one of the N.A.T.O. nations is the problem of propaganda attracting the attention it deserves. The minor members of this international club seem to be primarily concerned in selfish local squabbles. In America the immense latitude accorded to the press and radio and the unco-ordinated policies of the State Department, that seem to vary from day to day in chameleon-like fashion, result in a veritable Tower of Babel. France, torn by the stresses of internal politics, seldom speaks with the same voice for more than a few weeks at a time. West Germany is consistent in its determination to get all it can for Germany. Britain, struggling against inflation and competing wage claims, turns to sport, entertainment and dramatic social events for escape.

In most of these countries there is the embryo of an organization which might, if helped, become a major defence service. In the United Kingdon the Central Office of Information and the British Council, both constantly under attack by the press, work against heavy odds. It is certainly arguable that if these two bodies received the governmental and national support that they deserve, one more potent weapon would be added to the armoury of our defence.

This argument can be carried a good deal further without stretching it unduly.

There is certainly a case for stating that some wars may start from misunderstanding. Hostility, not amounting to actual violence, can begin by a lack of comprehension of the intention of others. This is particularly the case amongst primitive people who cannot be reached by the written word. Here radio can play a part of supreme importance—in both directions. A great deal of trouble is being fomented in the Middle East and in Africa by the inflammatory broadcasts from Cairo Radio. This hostile propaganda may quite well lead to the outbreak of war —for a cause which has not only been misrepresented but misunderstood. There has surely never been a greater need for a co-ordinated drive on the part of the N.A.T.O. nations to prevent this happening.

Such a drive might prevent small wars from starting, just as the "Great Deterrent" should put a stop to great wars. The world might then live in peace for a generation or more.

CHAPTER XI

"THE NEW LOOK"

IF the arguments put forward in the previous chapters are agreed, then the future shape of our armed forces can be determined.

Firstly, the Navy. The rocket-equipped and atomically-powered submarine capable of travelling submerged for a month at a time looks like being the capital ship. Its striking power will only be limited by the size of the A/H rocket it can carry. Operationally, it will be an immensely powerful submersible, with the hitting power of many battleships and the evasive qualities of the submarine. No seaboard will be safe from its hidden attack, and no city within many hundreds of miles of the shore can escape its attentions. Its rockets would be of the intermediate-range type, since it can approach within a relatively short distance of most of the important towns of the world. A reach of fifteen hundred miles would be sufficient, and that is nearly possible already.

The backer-up of the submarine would be the light carrier equipped with general purpose aircraft capable of carrying the A/H bomb. These carriers would be few in number, as the occasions on which they could operate with safety would be rare.

Other carriers of the auxiliary type might be found useful as convoy escorts and as an insurance against the recurrence of the conventional war against trade. As part of convoy escorts and for anti-submarine "killer" groups a strong force of frigates of the converted destroyer type will be required. And all must be equipped with the latest detection gear.

Finally, there may be some guided-missile ships, but these at the moment are of such an experimental character, and may be so vulnerable to air attack, that their worth is most uncertain.

The Army of the future will have, first of all, its highly mobile police force—the "Fire Brigade" that is needed to stifle the first signs of unrest. Next it will need a home defence force to deal with the many problems that may arise if our country is subjected to atomic/nuclear bombardment. Finally, it would seem logical to put it in charge of the I.C.B.M.'s, the I.C.G.M.'s, the I.B.M.'s and I.G.M.'s, which, after all, are only very long-range guns. The Royal Regiment of Artillery formed the first rocket batteries in the early eighteen hundreds. Common decency, as well as logic, insists that it should handle the rocket of the late 20th century!

The Air Force is at present in its usual dilemma. The weapons that it possesses are obsolescent. Just round the corner, according to the scientists who will be supported by the myriad civilians in the Ministry of Supply, there is something so wonderful that the R.A.F. could be abolished to-morrow without any loss of national security. While waiting for this perfect weapon which may take twenty years to produce, the "V" bombers, designed in 1945/46, in five years' time will still be lumbering through the sky at a mere 600 m.p.h. because the Ministry of Supply has produced nothing flyable or rocketable to replace them. Our fighters will still be single-seaters, or at the most two-seaters, of just over sonic speed. But in spite of this deplorable situation it may be that the Air Staff will somehow have contrived to obtain a selection of short-range guided missiles that will go far to solve the air defence problem. By the exercise of a great deal of patience and ingenuity they will also dispose of a few quite unusual aircraft that have a cruising speed of 1,500 m.p.h., a ceiling of 70,000 feet, an endurance of eight hours, a landing speed of 50 m.p.h., and, above all, the ability to carry the A/H bomb to any important target in Russian territory. This is the type of aircraft that alone can live in the rocket age and fulfil a useful function. But primarily the equipment of the Royal Air Force will be the pilotless ground to air missile, the humble but necessary transports, and the survey and communication aircraft that are required for day to day purposes in peace-time.

These are sweeping statements, and the future may prove them to be ill-founded. But there must always be the risk in prophecy, even when surmise is based on tenable arguments.

Some entirely new factor may arise; some new development in weapons of war; even some development in man's own consciousness of sin that will lead him away from war and towards the comfortable fields of everlasting peace.

But from a rational study of the present and from the possible consequences of our existing policies, a pattern does emerge. This pattern is formed by the basic influence of the A/H bomb and the rocket weapon upon the whole conception of offence and defence in the war of the future. What is happening is that the separate Services, the Navy, Army and Air, are being brought together as never before by the creation of the one overwhelming weapon.

When the three Services have been brought close together in their functions, as seems inevitable in the rocket age, it will be time to consider whether a unified Service is not the answer to the problems of overlapping, of coveting the neighbour's rocket, and of the centralization of authority in a rocket war. The numbers of officers and men required to man the various equipments that will provide our offensive and defensive power is bound to be greatly reduced from the present-day level. One I.C.B.M. operated by perhaps 200 specialists and soldiers will be the equivalent in striking power of very many brigades of artillery which normally require 20 men per gun to keep them in the field. A similar "run down" will be possible in the other two Services, and probably 150,000 to 200,000 regulars will be sufficient to man the Navy, Army and Air Force. Not more than 10,000 officers will be necessary, and it should be possible to obtain these through a common entry. Each officer, being a regular, can be expected to give an average of twenty years' service, so that the annual peace-time replacement programme will be about 500 new entrants, at the most. Dartmouth, Sandhurst and Cranwell could produce this output without difficulty, but probably the best solution would be to concentrate the whole entry at Sandhurst for a year, and then distribute the cadets who opt for the Navy or Air Force to Dartmouth or Cranwell for their second year. All suitable officers would come together again for a combined staff course lasting two years, after they had reached the rank of Lieutenant-Commander, Major or Squadron-Leader. For the next few years they would return to the Service of their choice, after which the best of them would come together again at the War College level for a further period of indoctrination in the theory and practice of inter-Service co-operation. A final tour with their own Service would lead to the emergence of those who are fit to hold the posts of Combined Services Chiefs.

This system and a comparable development in the enlistment and training of the "Other Ranks" should produce—if not a common Service—at least three Services with similar ideas about working as a team for the purposes of national defence.

A single Service would be likely to suffer from a lack of *esprit de corps*. In the Navy and Army many generations of commissioned officers and men have built up a tradition of loyalty and comradeship based on a close association of ideas. A uniform, a badge, stories of past achievement, regional ties born of birth and death in the same country, or the same port, have bound men together most firmly for a common purpose. The Royal Air Force has begun to form this association of ideas, but as yet the pattern is not clear. Nevertheless, all three Services, in varying degree, hold to their traditions, and these would disappear in the drabness of a fighting organization tailored to one uniform pattern. For this reason, amongst others, it would seem right to avoid too rigid an observance of the ideal of a single fighting Service.

Finally, and by no means least important, there must be the propaganda service. It would be worthwhile reactivating the Ministry of Information and giving it equal status with the Service Departments. It should be placed under the Minister of Defence as an equal member of the Services' team.

The business of the Ministry of Information would be to co-ordinate all the propaganda activities of Government Departments, notably that of the Foreign and Commonwealth Offices, the B.B.C. Overseas Broadcasts, and of the Public Relations Departments of the service and other ministries.

By this means alone will it be possible to wield the weapon of ideas really effectively—the long-range weapon of the future which may become even more effective in preventing wars than the A/H bomb and the I.C.B.M.

This is only a possibility, however, because even if major

wars are demonstrably impossible, it is doubtful if humanity will ever settle down to such a dead level of uniformity that there will be no competition for space, food or wealth. It is likely that for many generations there will be vast inequalities between the East and the West. Recent population statistics show clearly that the increase in the under-fed populations, in India, China and Japan, is such that enormous tensions are being created. While this continues, small wars, leading perhaps to bigger wars, may break out at any time. Those who have nothing to lose but their lives will risk them if there is a chance, however slim, of material gain.

In this respect, therefore, propaganda, the rocket and the atom bomb are not the ultimate solution.

Rudyard Kipling made a forecast many years ago of the conditions in which this world might live in peace and content-ment. He first postulated a world government that held the only sanction against ill-doing, an all-pervading and all-persuasive air power. Secondly, he considered that by rational birth control the total population of the earth would be maintained at about four hundred and fifty million, rather less than a fifth of its present content. This, he suggested, would allow of a minimum of 50 acres of cultivable land per person which, at the time he wrote this appreciation, would have made ample allowance for the necessary supplies. Finally, he based the whole organization of his world state on free com-munications. In this conception Kipling may be regarded as a most advanced thinker. He believed that the pressure of excess population might well continue to provoke wars. He realized that preventive medicine and modern hygiene might increase very materially the normal span of life. He had understood the implications of air power. Above all, he had accepted the need to abate nationalistic pretentions so that a world state and all that it implied could be formed. In recent years it has been fashionable to denigrate this "jingoistic, imperialistic and sabre-rattling writer of the Victorian era". But is he such a fool as he was described by writers and critics of the inter-war years, who have now largely sunk into the obscurity which they have deserved? The salvation of the free world seems to lie in the direction of his visions.

His conceptions of air power did not include the rocket and the atomic/nuclear missile. But he visualized other less brutal methods of control—noise, super-sonic and sub-sonic, only harmful for the moment and then to the nerves alone—light that in excess can be torturous. Annihilation on the atomic scale was not within his gentle thoughts. He believed in the cane applied to the right part of the peccant child—and are not most men and women children in essence?

If he was alive today he would very probably recommend the following cures for our present ills. Firstly, the establishment of a world government and the abolition of all barriers of colour, creed, economics or national pride. Secondly, the provision of a world police force, the main sanction of which would be air power. Thirdly, drastic birth control, particularly amongst the Oriental and Catholic races. This might well be the biggest problem of all in view of the age-old superstitions that still sway millions of people. Fourthly, completely free communications, such as Mr. Ernest Bevin prayed for when he said that he hoped to live to see the day when he could go to Victoria Station and buy a ticket to Moscow, certain of getting there without a passport, or customs interference or exchange control.

The outlook for such a development is not entirely unhopeful. Powerful forces are working both politically and economically towards a United States of Europe. Small but significant changes are occurring in international relationships. A Council of Europe, at present only a debating society, sits regularly at Strasbourg, and at Geneva the International Labour Office pursues, in a quiet but effective manner, the path towards agreement on labour affairs. It may be said, then, with some justice, that the most highly developed nations of the world have, for the present, before them the aim of federation and peace. Unfortunately there are other countries that have different views and are still many thousands of "thought miles" away from the Utopia of the world state.

Numbers of small tribes are clamouring for self-determination and their establishment as independent states. Because they speak some dialect that only a few thousand people understand, they lay claim to an individual culture that must at all costs be preserved. They may have no literature of worth, no art that by international canons of taste can be regarded as more than mediocre, no achievement in any form of useful productivity and above all no military power. Yet, since some centuries ago they lived a separate existence, they demand a position equal to that of the worthwhile nations of the world. When they are granted this position, to which in fact they have no right, they set up customs barriers to protect their inefficient industries, exchange control to hide the fact that their currency is valueless, and racial discrimination to prevent the more intelligent people of the world from establishing efficient commercial contact. Each one of these weak units is a potential source of trouble. It has not the resources with which to protect itself and its activities poison its neighbours. In the result it becomes a fomenter of small wars and possibly the origin of great wars.

This book does not concern itself over-much with ethics or sentiment. But it attempts to deal with the facts of defence and offence as they exist at present and as they may be in the future. Hence, when discussing the effects of nationalism, no consideration is given to religious or sentimental ideas. These, of course, have their place in politics and must guide our leaders in their attempts to reach a solution in the intractable problems that face them in North Africa and elsewhere. The dilemma in which the leaders find themselves is almost heartbreaking. On the one hand the United States—forgetting for a moment her obsession with the Russian danger—urges more and more concessions on Britain and France. On the other these two nations, being much nearer the immediate focus of trouble, see more clearly how everything is moving to Russia's advantage. The cleavage which hitherto our great enemy has failed to produce is, in a modified form perhaps, here today.

CHAPTER XII

THE MARCH OF COMMUNISM

AS long as the free nations presented a united front, and possessed military bases across the ocean highways, and so long as they spoke with one voice, Lenin's hope that Communism and Capitalism would clash in one final major war ending in the defeat of Capitalism seemed unlikely to be realized. For some years after the Hitler war this situation prevailed. Today in certain respects the scene is different.

Under the influence of a mass of woolly-headed idealists of which the U.S.A. and Britain seem to have an abundance, and from the attacks of Communist-inspired adventurers, the whole structure of N.A.T.O. defence is being undermined. The bases essential to this defence are no longer secure, and territories that were once reasonably friendly are now in the grip of hostile nationalist forces. Looked at from the point of view of conventional armaments the Communist countries are steadily improving their position. The erosion of the security of the free nations can proceed from within and without, and never will the temperature rise to a point where a major war must break out, and the A/H bomb be used.

It is very sad to think that the U.S.A., which has done much to protect the freedom of the world, should have gone so far in becoming the biggest promoter of Russia's interests by backing the aspirations of every adventurer that arbors the flag of Nationalism.

The United States forms an essentially self-contained organization, with practically every raw material available within her boundaries that is needed to assure a successful economy. Americans therefore cannot understand that the older civilizations of Europe, lacking many of these raw materials, require a colonial empire to supplement their own resources. The population is mainly drawn from emigrants escaping from the restrictions of life in Europe and impatient and querulously critical of other nations' policies. Much of this attitude arises from ancient grudges which are no longer valid (the hates of the Boston Tea Party are still very much alive). But mainly it is due to a general lack of education and the "small town" mentality. If, at some later date, a greater comprehension of what makes the rest of the world act as it does is established in the U.S.A., a big step forward towards the creation of a world state will have been made. Here again, intelligent propaganda can play an important rôle.

The policy of the United States, which is directed to the disruption of the old colonial empires, has been highly successful in the case of Holland, a country that surely should have been treated with great sympathy; fairly successful with Britain; and now approaching a major success in the case of France.

Having persuaded Britain to leave Palestine at the behest of the millions of Jewish voters in New York, the position of the British Army in Egypt was made intolerable, mainly by the encouragement of Egyptian nationalism. This encouragement may have been indirect, but it was effective. Today there remains of British influence in the Canal Zone only a civilian organization that is entirely at the mercy of a military adventurer—Colonel Nasser. This was only one part of the American success. From Egypt, arms, ammunition, and gangsters to use them, are pouring across North Africa into Algeria, Tunis and Morocco. What was once a peaceful and prosperous territory where Frenchman and Arab rubbed along together without too much distaste for one another, is now a region of flame, murder and mutilation. It seems a remarkable record, and yet not one American in a hundred thousand has the slightest conception of the damage to world peace that is being done by his country's anti-colonial policy. In two wars the Americans have played a great part in saving civilization. In the "hot peace" or "cold war" of the present day they seem determined to destroy it. Can their leaders, some of whom are men of the highest quality, persuade the 140 millions that inhabit the vast territory of the U.S.A. that in Europe there are people who have some sense, and a feeling of duty towards their more unfortunate fellows, and certain rights which have belonged to them for many generations? This is one of the vital problems of the day and, so far, there is little indication that the White House and the State Department are seriously attacking it.

It has been said rather unkindly of our Foreign Office that its policy is based, after lunch, on the telegrams it receives in the morning. The State Department policy seems to be guided in much the same way by the pressure groups that use the Congressional lobby to further their aims. The most powerful of these groups are, in order of precedence, export business, the presidents of the oil companies, and the representatives of Judaism in the United States. Depending upon which of these gets access to Congress on a given day, so the State Department's activities appear to develop.

The present situation in the Middle East seems to be a direct reflection of the powers of the oil lobby. Ordinary common sense would appear to indicate that the U.S.A. should join the Baghdad Pact, tell the Jews in Palestine to keep their fingers off the trigger, suppress the deplorable successor of the great Ibn Saud, and help the British and French to stabilize a situation which today is rapidly getting out of hand. On the contrary, Aramco, the great American oil complex in Arabia, is given licence to spend its money without any regard to the needs of the national and international policies of the free nations. In consequence at any moment a minor war may start that could trigger off a major conflagration leading to the use of the "Great Deterrent" in its fatal rôle of massive destruction. How is it that free economies can allow these things to develop? In spite of life-long convictions many honest people are being driven to believe that big business based on private enterprise, in itself a good thing, is a thoroughly bad development of a healthy plant. The trouble seems to come from the growth of monopolies, of monolithic structures devised by individuals as ruthless and as amoral as the great conquerors who ravaged the world in the bad old days.

If this distaste for the capitalist state continues to grow, as it may well do, the day of world communism is bound to come. The alternative is, of course, Kipling's conception of a world authority and individual self-sufficiency which many people would prefer.

This ideal is unlikely to be achieved for a very long time,

and, meanwhile, a viable system which will maintain the essentials of civil liberty and at the same time make headway against communism must be devised.

Such a system might well be based on the war-time controls that worked effectively, so far as Britain was concerned, from 1939 to 1952. These controls were, in fact, the reflection of an autocratic state functioning for the benefit of the mass and not of the individual. Because of the emergency the draconic regulations concerning trade, currency, transport, food, drink, agriculture, and many other facets of daily life, were accepted by the people, if not willingly (the black market throve), at least as a dire necessity. As soon as the emergency appeared to pass individualism clamoured for a return to the conditions that held before the war. The Labour Party was very reluctant to abandon controls, not because it believed that an emergency still existed, but because these regulations formed the basis of "Socialism in our time". When the Conservatives were returned to power the slogan became "Set the people free". This from the party's point of view may have been good politics, but it ignored the fact that while the hot war might have ended, the cold war continued. Nowhere has this slogan, which in regard to the colonies is common to both parties, been applied with more unfortunate consequences to our military strength than in Africa, Ceylon and Malaya. At one time the focus of a world-wide and firmly knit empire, Britain is now an overcrowded island living desperately in a struggle to maintain its very existence. The removal of internal controls and import restrictions has produced a galloping inflation which will be aggravated beyond measure as each part of the old Empire falls away, and no longer contributes to the maintenance of our prosperity. Further, every small unit that regains its independence, and with it a complete lack of security, is fair prey for our enemies.

Here is easy meat for the communist beast. Unless steps are taken to arrest this disintegration which has its counterpart in Western Europe it will not be necessary for us to wait until 1984 before "big brother will be watching us"—we shall be defeated by our own weaknesses—and the rocket and A/H bomb will have had nothing to do with this disaster.

L

Something can be done fairly quickly to stop the inflation in Britain that arises from internal causes. The present Government has made some progress in this direction, but labour generally, and the Trades Unions in particular, are far from grasping the urgency of our problem. Their education must proceed. It should not be impossible to negotiate with the "self-governing" colonies arrangements whereby their security was assured. This would involve some sacrifice of their prestige for a very real benefit. Perhaps if the U.S.A. was prepared to underwrite such arrangements the pill might be sugared. But there must be no more contracting out of the Commonwealth in the belief that, following the fatal example of India, security can be assured by neutralism, and that limited and underdeveloped economies can be self-sufficient. The tragedy of our situation today seems to lie in the fact that as soon as the strength of the Western nations was built up to the point where it was a real deterrent to aggression, this new factor—the national aspirations of their colonies—began to intrude. To what extent these aspirations have been inspired by Russia is not clear. But that she is taking advantage of them is abundantly plain. It would seem as though the Soviets, having decided that a head-on clash is not worthwhile, have launched a political campaign to destroy the foundations of our strength, the possession of bases and world-wide communications that are essential to success. In fact, they are cleverly extracting the back teeth which give power to our bite. Soon they may begin on our incisors! Thus all the technological skill of the Free World may well be unavailing. The A/H bomb stands idle on the touch-lines while the war of ideas is fought out in mid-field. It is for this reason that so much importance is attached in this book to political considerations, and to the overwhelming importance of skilful psychological warfare in our struggle for survival.

ENVOI

THIS analysis of the uses of the rocket and A/H warhead in the future has come full circle to the point where it seems clear that one part of this new weapon, the A/H bomb or warhead, is, by reason of its potency, unlikely ever to be used. It remains as a threat which may prevent any attempt by a great power to start a major war, but is probably unable, for reasons already discussed, to prevent small wars from breaking out. These little wars can at least be controlled by more conventional methods—police measures, in fact—but their occurrence can best be prevented by the intelligent use of propaganda.

The rocket, however, will not be idle. In its more peaceful applications it is working to advantage. Already the year 1957 is forecast as the period when man-made satellites will circle the earth, radiating to land stations the information about outer space that is gathered by the instruments they contain. Farther off, a great deal farther off, is the project to despatch a space ship to the moon. According to some scientists and to many enthusiasts there is no difficulty in realizing this aim, except perhaps the need of money. Other scientists are much more sceptical and point to our lack of knowledge regarding the conditions likely to be met during a lunar voyage. They paint a hideous picture of the probable effect on the human body of prolonged exposure to cosmic rays. Space, they say, is not empty but full of wandering bodies great and small, the refuse from long-dead stars, and the fragments of cosmic explosions. A space ship would be very lucky to avoid collision with these meteorites. The small objects might be harmless, but anything approaching the size of the mass that fell in Northern Siberia a hundred or more years ago would terminate the existence of the space ship abruptly.

Nevertheless, in the last fifty years there have been spectacular advances in the sum of human knowledge. Thus, only a fool would say that space travel is an impossibility. It is more than likely that the Astronomer Royal—reported to have referred unfavourably to the activities of the Interplanetary Society—was speaking without due consideration and in a fit of impatience with the press reporters who were questioning him too closely.

But apart from the matter of space travel there is the far more immediate problem of the utilization of rocket propulsion for normal peace-time transportation.

Starting with a simple example of what might quite easily be achieved in the fairly near future, there is the movement of first-class mail matter, valuable parcels, and "most important" documents. For these articles the I.C.B.M. would provide a reliable vehicle. Discharged from the new-fashioned London Airport the missile, loaded with diamonds, gold, and the thoughts of the Prime Minister of the day on the subject of the manufacture of dangerous drugs, would be projected towards New York. Rising to a height of some 400 miles or more, the space machine would cross the Atlantic in about fifty minutes. As it approached the American coast the radar operators at Idlewild would signal the air-brakes to open. At a reduced speed the approach to New York would continue, and the height would be reduced progressively. When on a ballistic path to the destination, at a height of 20,000 feet or so, the parachutes would be opened and quietly and safely the missile, still smoking faintly from the heat of its passage, would flop down on the airfield.

A simpler and possibly less expensive version of the I.C.B.M.—the I.C.G.M.—might be easier to handle. It would be a glorified version of the V1—with variable surface wings controllable in flight from the ground. Its speed would be less —something in the order of 2,000 m.p.h. maximum, and an average of 1,500 m.p.h. It would cross the Atlantic in $2\frac{1}{2}$ hours and would be able to carry a considerable load. In addition, it could take off and land under radio control, and so would be suitable not only for freight but also for passengers.

So, within a short space of time it should be possible to travel from London to New York with no greater boredom than today when being conveyed by our nationalized railways from Waterloo to Bournemouth. Many hours—no, days—will be saved. But what shall we do with the time thus spared to us? This is the big question presented by high-speed travel.

When the Comet 1 first flew on a regular service from

England to Singapore the most serious complaint that came from the passengers on this route was that they had no time to rest. No sooner—it seemed—than they had left the ground, settled into their seats, talked to the air hostess, made the acquaintance of the affable captain of the aircraft and had eaten and drunk to their satisfaction, than they were back on the ground being herded through customs and security control. This process was repeated at such short intervals that they reached their destination completely exhausted. How much more so will be the distraction of the 1,500 m.p.h. aircraft! The interference of the revenue and security controls will occur three times as rapidly, and the chance of getting a quiet snooze while the machine is airborne will be nil. It would seem that speed and stage-length are closely associated. For comfort's sake very high speed "aircraft" should only be used for one long flight, as for example across the Atlantic. On flights on which, for reasons of operating economy, landings at a number of airports, perhaps not more than 1,000 miles apart, or even less, are necessary, the best speed might well be as low as 350/400 m.p.h. In fact, the suburban transport of the future. A period of 2½ to 3 hours admits of the passengers composing themselves, resting, reading, and forgetting for a sufficient length of time the cares of daily life. The breaks for customs and security would not be quite so irritating if they were sufficiently far apart in time for a previous struggle with a truculent official to be almost forgotten. For these reasons it does not seem that the rocket will play an important part in passenger transportation for short distances.

For long stages it could take the place of the prop-jet and the pure jet. But this will not happen until the art of landing safely on the "rocket reversed" has been perfected. While it must be admitted that the speed of descent of the rocket car will be much reduced by the use of parachutes, there must be some other means, completely safe, of preventing the passengers being subjected to the sort of shock that the hardened parachutists have to endure. Of course, if the scheme recently put forward in an aviation magazine was adopted, even this obstacle to the rocket might disappear. It was humorously suggested that passengers, before embarking, should be given an injection which would put them to sleep for the period of the journey. They would be placed in plastic containers and slung, like sides of bacon, on racks in the aircraft. Thus they would be completely unaware of the acceleration due to take-off, of the boredom of the voyage, and of the risks and shock of landing by parachute. Incidentally, many more could be crammed into the rocket car than if conventional seating methods were employed, and great economy would be achieved. Of course, if things went wrong with the parachutes or landing rocket, the holocaust would be on a considerable scale, but this is a drawback which today is accepted without question. Conventional aircraft coming into service within the next year or two will carry over 100 passengers, and so far no one has suggested that there would then be too many eggs in one basket.

Of space travel much has been written by imaginative people, in many cases lacking any technical knowledge that would guide their pens. But what is clear is that if procreation proceeds at the present rate for the next 200 years, there will only be standing room on this planet. The colonization of other spheres will become imperative.

If, however, the fears of genetic scientists are justified, and that the atomic explosions that have taken place already are going to reduce the fertility of the human race, the problem may not become acute for many centuries. But what is in-escapable is that if the world avoids destruction by collision with another star in the millenia that are to follow, it will grow progressively so cold that life upon it, as we know it today, will be impossible. So, rocket exploration of space throughout the years may, in the end, lead to a transmigration of our population from a dying world to a new, comfortable and well-warmed planet. In the mists of time the work of Oberth, Dornberger, Schmidt, von Braun and their many colleagues will be forgotten. But the new people, living in contentment and for several hundred years each with a knowledge and wisdom beyond compare, on the successor to this odd little planet of ours, will owe their continued existence to these visionaries of the 20th century after Christ. The Great Architect of the Universe may well look down in some contentment on one of His enterprises that has proved successful.

As A footnote to the "Battle of the Sites" a Ministry of Information "hand-out" which was given to the Press on the 8th September 1944, is quoted in full. The gist of this document is accurate to the point where there is an inference that the battle was over. In fact this was not so, and some of the statistics given are faulty. Nevertheless, a picture is given of what was felt about the battle at the time, and as such it is of historical value.

Excerpt from The Times, *8th September, 1944*

"Giving a full account to a Press conference of the enemy's flying bomb attacks on this country, Mr. Duncan Sandys, M.P., Chairman of the Flying Bomb Counter-Measures Committee, said that 92 per cent of all the fatal casualties from the bombs occurred in the London region. He also revealed that during the 80-day attack 2,300 of the 8,000 bombs launched reached the London area.

Mr. Sandys said:

'Except possibly for a few last shots, the Battle of London is over. This battle against the flying bomb has been going on now for 18 months.

It was in April 1943 that the Chiefs of Staff sent me four rather vague reports from secret agents which suggested that the Germans were developing a long-range bombardment weapon of some novel type.

These four reports led us to suspect that the new weapon, if it existed at all, was being developed on the Baltic coast. Accordingly reconnaissance aircraft were sent to photograph the most likely areas in that region. Photographs obtained early in May shewed that at Peenemünde, on an island in the Baltic, there was what appeared to be a large experimental station. We went on photographing Peenemünde at frequent intervals. On a later photograph the expert interpreters drew our attention to a tiny blurred speck. On close examination it could be seen that the object had the shape of a miniature aeroplane. This was sitting on what appeared to be an inclined ramp fitted with rails.

A photograph taken on another occasion shewed that in the vicinity of the ramp the ground was blackened with dark streaks such as might have been caused by hot blast. Having regard to this and other information, it was deduced that the object seen must have been a pilotless, jet-propelled aircraft.

All doubts were removed when we discovered last November that the Germans were building all along the French coast from Calais to Cherbourg a whole series of concrete structures which had certain unmistakable features in common with those seen at the experimental station on the Baltic. Furthermore, we noticed that these sites in France were almost all of them orientated in the direction of London.

As a result of extensive air reconnaissance throughout the difficult winter months we eventually discovered over a hundred of these firing points. The British and American Air Forces started attacking these flying bomb sites last December, and continued incessantly throughout the winter and spring until every one of them was destroyed. The enemy tried to repair them. As they were repaired they were bombed again.

Heavy and persistent air attacks were kept up all through the winter. In the end the Germans abandoned these launching sites altogether and started round about last March constructing an entirely new series of firing points. These new sites took only about six weeks to construct and were so thoroughly camouflaged that it was practically impossible to detect them on air photographs until they had actually fired.

After the destruction of the first series of sites the Germans had to start again from scratch and it was, therefore, well into the summer before the second series were completed.

By this time our Intelligence Services had pieced together sufficient information about Hitler's secret V1 to enable us to go ahead with detailed arrangements for the defence of London. The plan provided for three defence belts—a balloon barrage just outside London, a gun belt beyond that, and beyond that again a fighter zone, and it had to be very flexible.

The attack started a few days after the landings in France. Our guns and balloons were already extensively sited around the British ports of departure, and, in accordance with the plan, the balloons and guns were immediately moved to prepared positions to the south-east of London. They began to come into action at once and within twenty-four hours they were beginning to take their toll of the bombs.

The bombs flew at a very high speed between 350 and 400 miles an hour and the enemy launched his bombs in salvoes. He also concentrated, so far as possible, the weight of the attack in periods of cloudy weather. On certain dull days as many as 200 flying bombs were launched within twenty-four hours. The height at which the bombs flew also presented the guns with difficulty.

Originally we had deployed some 500 balloons but when it was seen that the bombs were consistently flying low the barrage was rapidly thickened up to nearly 2,000.

The ballons were, of course, the last line of defence. Being in the back row they only got the birds that had been missed by the fighter and gun belt in front. Nevertheless, they made a substantial contribution. Of the bombs which entered the barrage area nearly 15% were brought down.

During the period preceding the invasion a large proportion of our anti-aircraft guns were sited around the embarkation ports and assembly areas in the south and west. When the flying bomb attack started these guns were immediately moved to prepared sites along the southern edge of the balloon barrage, stretching roughly from Maidstone to East Grinstead.

About the middle of July it was decided to take the bold step of moving the entire A.A. belt down to the coast, so that the guns should get an uninterrupted field of view.

From that time onwards the guns never looked back. In the first week after the redeployment the guns shot down 17% of the bombs which entered the gun belt and in the last week it was 74%.

The A.A. defences have been in action day and night during the last two and a half months. The people of London owe much to the men and women of Anti-Aircraft Command and, in particular, to General Pile, to whose energy and personal leadership these achievements are in large measure due.

During the first few weeks of the flying bomb attacks

the fighters shot down over a thousand flying bombs. In this battle our fighters were faced with a number of difficulties. Only our fastest fighters possessed the high speed needed to overtake the bomb in level flight. The other types, in order to obtain an interception, had to dive on to the bomb from several thousand feet above.

It was necessary to maintain constant standing patrols over land and sea throughout the twenty-four hours.

Another awkward problem was that of seeing the bomb at all. Pilots on patrol had the greatest difficulty in spotting this very small, fast-moving object several thousand feet below. Over land help could be given to the pilots by means of a running commentary over the radio telephone, telling them where the bomb was in relation to various landmarks.

In the hours of darkness it was, of course, easy enough to spot the flaming tail of the flying bomb many miles away, but in order to bring down the bomb the pilot must fire his gun at a range of about 300 yards. If he fired when too far away he probably would not destroy the bomb. If he fires when too near, the bomb may blow up and destroy him.

Our scientists gave much attention to this problem, which for a long time baffled us. Experiments were carried out with various elaborate radio equipments. Meanwhile Professor Sir Thomas Merton produced a simple and ingenious range-finder which proved to be the complete answer. It was so simple that the whole device cost little more than one shilling.

Since the start of the bombardment our fighter aircraft have brought down over 1,900 flying bombs.

As was noticed by many people a small proportion of the bombs came in by night from a due easterly direction. This puzzled us a little at first, because, as far as we knew, there were no flying sites either in Belgium or Holland. However, we very soon obtained information that these flying bombs were being launched, not from the ground, but from aircraft. Specially adapted Heinkel bombers approached our coast, 97 were brought down by the defences and only 4 got through to London.

This vast increase in the effectiveness of the defences was, of course, reflected immediately in the casualty figures. At the beginning, on an average, one death for every bomb launched. At the end, three bombs had to be launched to kill one person.

During five days in July a light scale attack was made upon Portsmouth and Southampton. However, the great majority of the bombs fell in the sea or in open country. The weapon was clearly not accurate enough to be used against targets of this size.

During the rest of the time the attack was aimed at the unique target of London. About 92% of all the fatal casualties occurred in the London region.

Although many hundreds of bombs were shot down by the guns along the south coast, only eleven of these fell in built up areas. The understanding and restraint of the people living inside various defence zones of Kent, Sussex and Surrey are deserving of great praise. By their readiness to accept their share of London's dangers the people of "bomb alley" played a notable part in keeping down the overall casualties.

I am very glad to have the opportunity of expressing formally, on behalf of His Majesty's Government, our appreciation of the help which our American allies have given us in the battle against the flying bomb. They have thrown themselves into the job of beating the bomb with just as much determination and enthusiasm as if New York or Washington had been the victim of the attack.

American batteries provided about one-eighth of the total number of heavy A.A. guns along the south coast. Some of their very latest equipment was used with our heavy guns. The biggest American contribution has, however, been in the field of offensive air operations.

Ever since Bomber Command made its great raid on Peenemünde in August of last year, the British and American Air Forces have been conducting a continuous battle against Hitler's secret weapon. Altogether they have dropped on these targets over a hundred thousand tons of bombs. All this has, of course, not been done without loss. On these operations the British and American Air Forces have together lost nearly 450 aircraft, involving a loss of approximately 2,900 pilots and aircrew.

Bombing cannot, of course, be separated from Intelligence. In the battle against the flying bomb Intelligence Services, our agents in enemy territories, the Air Reconnaissance Squadrons, and the Photographic Interpretation Unit, have played a particularly responsible part.

Large stocks of flying bombs were stored in tunnels and

caves not far from Paris. The entrance of these storage depots were reported and bombers went out to destroy them. Agents reported that the enemy was moving his stocks to other depots. Many of these were in their turn discovered and destroyed. Then a train loaded with some 200 flying bombs was detected and information was passed back to England in time for our bombers to go out and blow up the train before it moved off.

But for our interference there can be little doubt that the bombardment would have started in the early months of this year. We now know, for instance, that not only engineers but actual flying bomb firing units were already on the French coast waiting to begin operations last January. Had the attacks started then the winter conditions would have seriously affected the efficiency of our defences. For days at a time fighters and balloons would have been grounded by bad weather.

Most serious of all, the bombardment would have lasted very much longer. All along we have known that there was only one completely effective way of putting a final stop to flying bomb attacks. That is, by actually capturing the firing sites. This has been happening in the last few days. The destruction of the first hundred launching sites not only delayed the start of the attack but also forced the enemy, for the sake of concealment, to construct his second series on simpler but less efficient lines.

The visitation which London has so bravely endured has been painful enough. Had it not been for the vigilance of our Intelligence Services, the unrelenting efforts of the British and American Air Forces, and the effectiveness of the defences, London's ordeal might well have been many times more severe.'

A scale model of a flying bomb 18 in. long stood on the table in front of Mr. Sandys while he made his report. When he invited questions the first put to Mr. Sandys concerned V2.

'I am a little chary of talking about V2,' he replied. 'We do know quite a lot about it. In a very few days' time I feel that the Press will be walking all over these places in France, and will know a great deal more then than we do now.'

Referring to the fact that a proportion of the bombs dropped in southern districts of London he said, 'I think there was a tendency to fall short.'

General Pile disclosed that just under one half of his command fighting the flying bombs were women. Eventually there were 800 heavy and nearly 2,000 light guns, and 20 American batteries under his command. The 'hottest' twenty-four hours occurred when the gunners fired 24,000 heavy, and 45,000 light rounds. The total of bombs brought down by his command was 1,560.

Air Marshal Sir Roderick Hill said that the machines used by A.D.G.B. were the Tempest, Mustang, and the latest Spitfire. The finest 'bag' for one pilot is just over 60. This was achieved by Squadron-Leader Berry in a Tempest.

Air Vice-Marshal Gell said that the balloons brought down 279. 'We were in very much the same position as a goal-keeper,' he said.

Others present on the conference platform were Mr. Brendan Bracken, Minister of Information, Air Marshal Sir Norman H. Bottomley, and Brigadier-General Overil A. Anderson (Deputy Commander for Operations 8th U.S.A.A.F.)."

The Rôle of P.R./P.I. in the German V Weapon Programme

by D. R. KENDALL[1]

P.R./P.I. played a major part in the intelligence war against the German V weapons. There had been rather vague rumours about German development of V weapons, notably rockets, since very early in the war but the first more positive hint came early in 1943, actually January, when the Allied Central Interpretation Unit was advised that the Peenemünde area on the Baltic coast might be tied in with long-range rocket development. It was understood that the area was closed to the public.

As a result of these rumours, arrangements were made to photograph the Peenemünde area and this was successfully completed on the 9th of February 1943, revealing for the first time the static rocket test stands. Their significance at this stage was not fully understood. It is of some interest that in a briefing given to the interpretation unit on the 19th of March 1943 by the War Office, it was suggested, following technical studies, that a rocket if it could be built would be of a two-stage compound type with a maximum range of 130 miles, a weight of $9\frac{1}{2}$ tons, a length of 95 feet, a warhead of $1\frac{1}{4}$ tons and a length of projector of 100 yards.

In many respects the briefing was of course incorrect, as we now know, but it proved nearer the truth, except for the method of projection, than the guesses later in the war once we had seen on photographs the actual rocket. A weight of 45 tons with a 10-ton head was then predicted by some scientists. The Air Ministry first took note of the possibility of V weapons in April 1943 and the P.I. unit was instructed to inaugurate a search of all areas within 130 miles of London and Southampton for any suspicious activity which might be associated with special weapons. At the same time Mr. Duncan Sandys was appointed to report direct to Mr. Churchill on the day to day findings.

---

[1] *Note.*—Mr. Kendall was a member of P.I.U. from 1940 until the end of the war. He is now engaged in photographic survey in Canada.

On the 20th of April, 1943, arrangements were made for all areas within 130 miles' radius of London and Southampton to be photographed. This work, as with all photographic reconnaissance work required in the European theatre, was shared by both the R.A.F. and the U.S.A.F. photographic reconnaissance squadrons.

During the following weeks, numerous meetings were held between the interpreters in the P.I. unit assigned to this project and various scientists who were approaching the subject of rockets from a theoretical basis. In other words they were attempting to advise the interpreters what to look for. At this stage the whole investigation and emphasis was on rockets and any suggestion that new weapons other than rockets might be involved was discounted. Moreover the interpreters were instructed to look for launching rails to start the rockets on their way and were advised that due to the weight of the rocket any sites to be used would be rail-served. Initial searches were therefore confined to the railways and any spur lines were followed up most carefully.

At the end of April 1943, after photographing Peenemünde a number of times, it was possible to conclude that this was an experimental area, employing explosives and used for the testing of these and projectiles. It was further concluded that the projectiles had not so far gone beyond the experimental stage, although none of them had been seen, and that in view of this the heavy long-range rocket was not yet an immediate menace. Mr. Duncan Sandys reported thus to the Cabinet.

In May 1943, a month later, a large concrete structure in north France at a place called Watten was observed for the first time. Since Watten did not conform with any known military installation, it naturally became highly suspect in connection with V weapons. Consequently by June 1943 Mr. Sandys felt compelled to report to the Cabinet that in his opinion a long-range rocket probably existed and might even be in limited production. Re-examination of all areas within 130 miles of London was therefore put in hand once more.

By now Peenemünde was being photographed by our P.R. units if possible twice a week and great activity was noted on all occasions. On the 16th of June a vertical column 40 feet in height was noted on the foreshore but was not identified at that time. It was, of course, one of the rockets sitting on its fins ready for firing. However, on the 28th of June 1943 three rockets, described at the time as torpedo-like objects 38 feet long, were seen for the first time in the open. On the 2nd of July 1943 the P.R. unit issued a report based on some photographs obtained on 22nd April 1943 reporting some aircraft with a wing span of 30 feet and concluding from the blast marks behind them that these were either jet- or rocket-propelled. This was the first time that jet aircraft had been observed in Germany and, while a matter of great significance, it was decided that these were not associated with the secret weapons. These were actually Messerschmitt 163 (rocket-propelled) fighter aircraft and were observed at the airfield associated with the Peenemünde base. Early in July the Prime Minister, Mr. Churchill, directed that the maximum possible contribution was to be made by the P.R./P.I. units, who were to be given any necessary facilities and manpower required to meet commitments. Fortunately the resources were already available.

By the end of July 1943 Mr. Duncan Sandys was able to summarize for the Cabinet the current state of the investigation. The summary was somewhat as follows:

"By April 1943 the accumulation of intelligence reports indicated the development of very long-range rocket projectiles at Peenemünde and the frequent photographic reconnaissance of Peenemünde since has tended to confirm this conclusion. An object 38 feet long, quite evidently the rocket, has been seen in the open. Having regard to the size of projectile, it should be taken as certain that the projector sites will be rail-served. Certain unexplained installations, rail-served, have been observed in north France, notably at Wissent, Marquise and Watten."

On the 12th of August 1943, following various further photographic flights over Peenemünde and observation of increased activity, it was decided that Peenemünde should be bombed in strength by the R.A.F., and the P.I. unit was instructed to prepare the necessary target material for briefing the crews. This attack took place on the night 17/18 August 1943 and was carried out from a very low altitude. The bomber crews had been advised of the great importance of the target and were asked to accept any risk to destroy it. The attack was carried out in moonlight and 40 bombers were lost. On the following day, 19th August 1943, the P.R. unit was successful in obtaining photographs of Peenemünde from which to assess the damage. The attack had been very success-ful and had destroyed a number of the permanent buildings. It is now known that it caused serious disruption and set back the whole rocket programme, which we now know as the V2 programme, by many months.

Meanwhile on the 27th of August 1943, the U.S. 8th Air Force with their heavy bombers attacked the construction at Watten. Photographs obtained three days later showed that this attack had been most successful and it was assessed by the interpreters that construction had been set back at least three months. The extent of the importance attached to the site by the Germans became clear when a few days later it was observed on air photographs that the German Air Force had brought in large quantities of anti-aircraft batteries to protect the Watten site. We now know that no less than 6,000 work-men were employed on the Watten construction.

Photography on a large scale was continued throughout September 1943 and a number of new constructions of a heavy concrete nature were reported in north France. Most of them were still in a very early stage of construction and it was obvious that they could not be used for a long time. It was also noted that repair work to Watten, following the U.S.A.F. raid, was still at a standstill although the flak defences were being reinforced. Obviously, however, early in October 1943 the enemy had a change in plan and the flak batteries were withdrawn from Watten and the site was abandoned tem-porarily. Consequently we reduced the photographic flying from twice weekly to once a month for the Watten site.

Towards the end of October 1943 a further meeting was held at the Ministry of Supply at which it was decided by their technicians that the production of a rocket with a range of 130 miles with a 14-ton explosive head was feasible and would not be too onerous in manhours. In view of this rather alarming conclusion it was decided to photograph all areas within 250 miles of London. It was also about this time that photographs were obtained showing considerable activity near the village of Mimoyecques. This consisted of a new spur line from the railway which entered the side of a hill and came out the far side. Meanwhile on the top of the hill above where the railway line ran were a number of rather artificial-looking haystacks. This particular area was watched in some detail over the next few months and was in fact the site of another form of V weapon although rather impractical and

M

destined never to be used. It was to consist of long tubes buried in the ground inclined at an angle of 45° which were to be gun barrels firing at one-minute intervals a small projectile direct on to London. Once the work had progressed to a certain stage, the site was severely damaged by our bombers, and never came into operation.

At the end of October all areas within 150 miles of London were once more placed on the programme for rephotography. This was the third time that this area had been totally photographed and each time this involved a very major effort by the P.R.U.s, R.A.F. and U.S.A.F. To photograph this area at the necessary scale, 1/10,000, involved about 100 sorties each time. One sortie would normally produce about 1,000 photographs involving in turn a very large effort in detailed examination of the pictures.

At the beginning of November 1943 a report was received from an agent, employed by a construction firm, that his firm had been engaged to build 8 sites in north France, the nature of which were not clear to him. It was therefore arranged that these 8 sites would be photographed by our P.R.U. These photographs were obtained on the 3rd of November 1943. The report issued on the 5th of November by the P.I. unit states:

"At each place some activity is seen, but if these are rocket projector sites, they at present bear little or no resemblance to any installations which have hitherto come under observation in connection with the investigation. There are however a number of features at each of these sites which make it clear that all are similar."

The interpretation report then went on to point out that there were no railway lines anywhere near the sites which were only served by roads and that each site was being constructed in a wood, presumably for camouflage purposes.

In order to get pictures which would show even greater detail arrangements were then made for photographs to be obtained from a low altitude by one of our tactical reconnaissance squadrons as soon as suitable weather conditions were available. For this purpose suitable weather conditions meant low cloud to give the aircraft protection until the site was reached.

By this time the subject of German V weapons was assum-

ing rather major importance. Because of its possible serious-
ness it was being handled as a Cabinet matter. The extent of
the threat was still not known, however, and it seemed
difficult to measure it. The scientists advising the Cabinet
were themselves divided, some taking the view that the threat
was most serious and others that it might even be a hoax
designed to buoy up the spirits of the German people and to
draw off bombing from German cities on to useless targets.
The German propaganda machine under Herr Goebbels was
making daily loud threats and hints about the wonderful new
weapons and the destruction which they would cause.

Accordingly the Prime Minister decided, in an attempt to
resolve the matter, that Sir Stafford Cripps should assess all
the evidence with a view to drawing conclusions on whether
the threat existed or was a hoax, and how serious it might
be. A meeting was therefore called for the 8th of November
1943 at which all the evidence was reviewed.

The evidence from non-photographic sources, which was
somewhat sparse and indefinite, was quickly disposed of. The
evidence from propaganda sources was considered in some
detail and it was pointed out that the enemy never made a
sustained threat, designed obviously to buoy up their own
people, unless there was some truth behind it. It was suggested
that threats of this type could have a salutary effect on the
people for about six months but if after this period the threat
failed to materialize serious repercussions in the dropping of
morale would ensue. On this basis propaganda analysis considered that the weapon was due to be launched in December
1943 or January 1944. This was indeed, as we now know,
close to the target date.

Following the propaganda evidence, the major part of the
day was given over to a detailed reassessment of the photographic evidence, which was the only positive evidence at
that time available.

Meanwhile following the finding of the new type sites in
north France, non-rail-served, which had been reported on the
5th of November 1943, a detailed re-examination had been
made of all recent photography and as a consequence by
midnight on 7th November 1943, no less than 19 sites of
this type had been observed in the very early stages of construction. None was rail-served. At the end of the meeting
with Sir Stafford Cripps, therefore, it became necessary for
the interpretation unit to state that 19 sites of a new type had

been located which might be connected with V weapon activity and the nature of which were not yet fully understood. It was explained that the information was still being developed and studied and had not even been put in report form for assessment by the War Office and Air Ministry branches. The reason for associating these 19 sites with V weapons was that they did not appear to have any connection with known military installations and in the case of a few of them, the agent, as already reported, had hinted at some secret significance. The meeting was therefore adjourned by Sir Stafford Cripps for two days on this rather surprising note, in order to give the P.I. unit sufficient time for more detailed studies.

On the 10th of November 1943 the meeting with Sir Stafford Cripps resumed and the interpretation unit was able to report that in the two-day interval, low oblique photographs of the sites had been obtained and moreover a total of 26 sites had now been located. It was also possible to state that each site had a platform which pointed in the direction of London and in addition there were three ski-shaped buildings which in P.R. opinion were intended for storage. The report also stated that there did not seem to be any indication that the sites were intended for the firing of rockets, which were supposed at this time to weigh 45 tons and would therefore have required heavy handling gear.

Following the meeting, Sir Stafford Cripps felt able to report to the War Cabinet that in his opinion V weapons definitely existed, since the amount and nature of the activity being devoted to the projects by the Germans was too great to be merely a diversionary hoax.

It now, obviously, became a matter of the greatest importance to assess the nature and purpose of the new sites in north France which were given the name of Bois Carré sites. These sites were being built by contractors who had obviously been handed plans. By obtaining new photographs of the whole area, it was not long before the P.I. unit had identified 96 sites, actually the total that was built. As with any contractors, the approach to construction was somewhat different from one site to another. Consequently one contractor would concentrate on the construction of certain buildings ahead of others while another contractor would put equal effort into all buildings simultaneously. As a result, however, it was possible to see that each site consisted of a number of buildings of a standard size but that the layout differed somewhat because of the shape of woods and the nature of topography. However by examining all 96 sites together it was quickly possible, by taking one building from one and one from another, to prepare a detailed plan of a typical site in more or less the finished condition. The process then started of assessing the nature of each building individually.

The three ski-shaped buildings were quickly put in the category of storage buildings for the weapon to be used. They had no windows and thick walls. Each was about 270 feet long. The curved ends caused some thought but it was quickly concluded that the object to be stored was of some length and therefore could not be removed from a normal building that had a blast wall in front of the entrance. The only way, therefore, to protect against blast would be by having the curved entrance. This assumed, of course, that the object to be stored was explosive.

The entrance to the skis was about 9 feet wide and it was not therefore possible, based on the evidence of the skis alone, to say that the site was not destined for rockets. The rockets which we had seen in the open at Peenemünde could, with difficulty, by removing the tail units, have been manœuvred round the curves and got into the ski-shaped buildings.

Attention was then given to the layout of the paths. This was important since obviously the layout indicated, as it were, flow. It was possible, for instance, to see that the weapon arrived by road and passed through a rectangular-shaped building which had large doors at each end and thus fed on to the site. From this building the paths led to the storage skis. From the skis, further paths led to a square-shaped building known as the square building, and from there to the concrete platform which pointed in the direction of London. There was a further rectangular building which in turn also fed to the firing platform.

Attention was next devoted to the platform pointing at London. This consisted of a concrete slab in front of which there were 8 pairs of studs built in concrete embedded in the ground. These studs were not unlike the foundations which would be used for the steel uprights which would support a bridge.

The implication of the studs was immediate since it showed that a ramp would be built with its base at the concrete slab and supported by vertical posts embedded in the studs. This ramp would be pointing directly at London but, since the studs stretched for approximately 130 feet in front of the concrete slab, it must be concluded that the ramp would be at a fairly low angle. The significance of this meant that the weapon could not be a rocket which would always have to be fired vertically to start it on its course and must therefore be something with wings which had lift. It was therefore possible to draw the conclusion that it was not a rocket but a flying bomb.

Passing to the square-shaped building, it was also noted that in every case this was aligned exactly parallel with the firing ramp and with its entrance pointing towards London. It was not difficult to conclude, therefore, that this was the building in which the control mechanism for guiding the flying bomb would be set in motion.

Going back to the ski-shaped buildings, it was quite obvious that if the weapon was indeed a flying bomb it could not be stored with its wings on in the ski-shaped building. From the shape of the paths, therefore, it was clear that the weapon would be taken to the square building and that assembly would take place there. Presumably the wings were then attached. This was confirmed admirably by the shape of the square-shaped building which looked not unlike a small hangar and had a hangar door with a width of 21 feet. It was therefore concluded that the weapon was a flying bomb controlled by an automatic pilot set in motion in the square building with the flying bomb pointing exactly in the direction in which it should travel and that it would have a wing span of less than 21 feet. After assembly the flying bomb would be taken to the firing ramp and that some method for catapulting it or sending it on its way would follow, the device for doing this coming from the other rectangular building which led to the firing point by a different path. Thus by the end of November 1943, although it had not yet been seen, the form of the weapon was well understood.

In the P.I. unit there were many sections which specialized in different aspects of the enemy's activity. One section was devoted to detailed studies of German aircraft and the German aircraft industry. Accordingly at this point the officer in charge of this section, Flight-Officer Babington-Smith, was advised that a flying bomb with a wing span of about 20 feet was probably the weapon and she was asked if she had observed this anywhere in Germany. She pointed out that a few months earlier she had reported certain small aircraft with a wing span of 20 feet at the airfield at Peenemünde near one of the aircraft test houses. It had not been possible at this time to state very much about them or that they were the missing weapon. However with this tie-back to Peenemünde, as with the rockets, she put in hand a detailed investigation of the Peenemünde area and within 24 hours had found the missing flying bomb on a ramp near a beach adjacent to Peenemünde. The photographs showing this had in fact been in our possession for about a week. The evidence was thus complete.

The Peenemünde rocket development belonged to the army whereas the flying bomb was a German Air Force development and took place at a different site. Having located the ramp with the flying bomb in place, it was possible to use old photographs obtained on previous occasions to study what had happened. At the site there were no square buildings or other installations as in north France but merely the small firing ramps. Over the course of a year or more, four different ramps had been built of different designs and it was clear that the final design was that to be used in north France, being of similar length. This ramp had only been completed in August 1943 and the first evidence of any activity on Bois Carré type sites, going back over old photographs, was in September 1943, just one month later. This activity consisted only of the moving of construction materials to some of the sites. By November 1943 the story was reasonably complete.

From this point on, the P.I. investigation was more routine but it took on very large proportions. It became necessary to watch all 96 sites and the method of assessing points to each site was worked out. It was possible to calculate that it would take 140 days to build a site so it was now known more or less the earliest date at which firing could start. This would be early in 1944. Points were allotted to each building so that the total points for any site were 100. Thus, if, for instance, one of the skis was valued at 10 points, and was about 50% constructed, it would contribute 5 points to the total.

Target material was then prepared for all 96 sites and as soon as a site reached 70 points, in other words 70% of completion, it was put on the bombing list. Following attack, photographs would be obtained and if damage had been done the necessary number of points would be deducted. As soon as a site fell below 60 points, it came off the bombing list. All this involved a great deal of work and a great deal of photographic flying but it was highly effective and meant that the bombing effort was always devoted to the most advanced site. Eventually by April 1944 all sites had been reduced to a safe category and the Germans had to abandon the whole programme.

Having realized that the Bois Carré sites were a failure, the Germans switched to a new programme consisting of a modified site to which the name Belhamelin was given, called after the first of these sites observed. 156 of these sites were built in all and they consisted only of the firing ramp and the square building. They were, in effect, field artillery units and represented a very poor bombing target. P.R.U. watched these being constructed and noted that the Germans would lay the concrete and then, apparently, abandon the site. It was therefore concluded that the square building would be pre-fabricated and that the ramp would only be assembled immediately prior to firing. On the 11th of June 1944 some photographs were obtained which showed the firing ramps being assembled at some of these sites and a telephone message to the Air Ministry, on a prearranged basis, advised them that firing could probably be expected within 48 hours. The first flying bomb came over on 13th June 1944.

Unfortunately it had not been possible to attack the Belhamelin type sites in the same way as the Bois Carré sites due to the necessity of switching the whole of the Allied bombing effort on to support of the Normandy landings. It had become necessary to accept some measure of attack on London in order to ensure the success of the landing operations. It was correctly assessed, however, that the number of flying bombs which could be fired from the Belhamelin sites would be quite low and indeed the maximum fired on any one night was about 250. Bombs could not be stored at the sites and had to be brought up by truck.

At the Bois Carré type sites, the storage available in the skis was sufficient for 20 flying bombs. With the 96 sites, it had been planned to fire, if possible, 2,000 flying bombs per night. It can well be appreciated what effect there would have been on London if indeed the firing had started in January 1944 instead of in June and had been on the scale planned. As it was, the damage was significant enough.

It should be mentioned that the Belhamelin sites were not

left completely unmolested. It was concluded that the right solution to reduce firings was to attack the storage sites. Obviously, since they could not store the flying bombs at the sites, there must be large storage depots further behind. It was concluded that the big storage depots fed by railway must be in the Paris area. These were found on photographs and sufficient bombing capacity was found to damage them seriously and thus reduce the firing to some extent.

Finally, parallel with all the investigations taking place in north France and the observation at Peenemünde, observation was kept on the other rocket experimental stations in Germany including that at Blizna in Poland, and an experimental flying bomb (V1) site at Zinnowitz on the Baltic coast which was the main testing area. In East Prussia, near Königsberg, were also found some duplicates of the Bois Carré type sites where obviously the troops intended to man the sites were trained. Other sites at Kummersdorf and Fredrichshafen were also watched.

Again much effort was devoted to studying the sources of manufacture. From the photographs the type of transport being used to move rockets and flying bombs to the front on the railways were discovered and by photographing the railway lines it was possible to track back to the factories producing the weapons. Everything pointed to Niedersachs-werfen being the key point, this being an underground factory in the Hartz Mountains. The type of vehicle being used to move the fuels, notably alcohol and liquid oxygen and hydrogen peroxide needed for the firing of the rockets, were found and located, in fact virtually all the plants producing these materials. It was thus known where the weapons were being produced, the sources of supply of the fuels, and the communication routes being used to bring the rockets to their firing points. To knock these out, however, would have involved major diversions of bombing from targets which at this stage were rapidly winning the war. Consequently a small measure of firing by the V2s had to be accepted. The fact is, however, that had the threat been more serious, the Allies were far from impotent to bring it to a stop and actually had many strings to their bow. In other words the information was reasonably total.

INDEX

187